Marda Brown

Bookcase

Stories

Contents • Stories

The Little Boy's Secret

DAVID L. HARRISON

One day a little boy left school early because he had a secret to tell his mother. He was in a hurry to get home, so he took a short cut through some woods where three terrible giants lived. He hadn't gone far before he met one of them standing in the path.

When the giant saw the little boy, he put his hands on his hips and roared, "What are you doing here, boy? Don't you know whose woods these are?"

"I'm on my way home," answered the little boy.

"I have a secret to tell my mother."

That made the giant furious. "Secret?" he bellowed. "What secret?"

"I can't tell you," said the little boy, "or it wouldn't be a secret any more."

"Then I'm taking you to our castle!" said the giant. Stooping down, he picked up the little boy and popped him into his shirt pocket.

Before long the first giant met a second giant who was twice as big, three times as ugly, and four times as fierce.

"What's that in your pocket?" he asked the first giant.

"A boy," he answered. "Says he has a secret that he won't tell us."

When the second giant heard that, he laughed a wicked laugh. "Won't tell us, eh?" he chuckled. "Well, we'll just see about that! To the castle with him!"

The giants thumped on down the path. In a short time they came to a huge stone castle beside a muddy river.

At the door they met the third giant, who was five times bigger, six times uglier, and seven times fiercer than the second giant.

"What's that in your pocket?" he asked the first giant.

"A boy," he answered.

"A boy!" chuckled the third giant. He brought his face close to the pocket and peered in.

"He has a secret he won't tell us," said the first giant.

When the third giant heard that he laughed a terrible laugh.

"Won't tell us, eh?" he asked. "Well, we'll just see about that! On the table with him!"

The first giant took the little boy from his pocket and put him on the kitchen table. Then all three giants gathered round and peered down at him.

The little boy looked at the first giant. He looked at the second giant. He looked at the third giant. They were truly enormous and dreadful to behold.

"Well?" said the first giant.

"We're waiting," said the second giant.

"I'll count to three," said the third giant. "One… two…"

The little boy sighed a big sigh.

"Oh, all right," he said. "I suppose I can tell you. But if I do, you must promise to let me go."

"We promise," answered the giants. But they all winked sly winks at one another and crossed their fingers behind their backs because they didn't really mean to let him go at all.

The little boy turned to the first giant. "Bend down," he said. The giant leaned down and the little boy whispered into his ear.

When the giant heard the secret, he leaped up from the table. His knees shook. His tongue hung out.

"Oh, no!" he shouted. "That's terrible!" And he dashed from the castle, ran deep into the woods, and climbed to the top of a tall tree. He didn't come down for three days.

The second giant scowled at the little boy.

"What's wrong with him?" he asked.

"Never mind," said the little boy. "Just bend down."

The second giant leaned down and the little boy stood on his toes and whispered into his ear.

When the giant heard the secret, he leaped up so fast he knocked his chair over. His eyes rolled. His ears twitched. "I have to get away," he roared. He raced from the castle into the hills and crawled into the deepest, darkest cave he could find.

The third giant frowned down at the little boy.

"What's wrong with them?" he asked.

"Never mind," said the little boy. "Just bend down."

The giant leaned down and the little boy climbed

on to a teacup and whispered into his ear.

When the giant heard the secret, he jumped up so fast that he ripped the seat of his trousers. His teeth chattered. His hair stood on end. "Help!" he cried. "Help!"

And he dashed from the castle and dived head first into the muddy river.

The castle door had been left open, and since the giants had promised the little boy that he could go, he walked out and went home.

At last he was able to tell his mother his secret; but she didn't yell and run away. She just put him to bed and gave him some supper.

The next morning when the little boy woke up, he was covered from head to toe with bright red spots.

"Now I can tell *everybody* what my secret was," he said with a smile. "My secret was … I'M GETTING THE MEASLES!"

All the Way from China

PAT BORAN

Chapter One

One morning Shelley's teacher Ms Garland came into the classroom and handed each of the children a plain white envelope. Inside each envelope was a piece of paper. On Shelley's was written:

> My name is Tomi Wong.
> I'm from Ningbo in China.
> I'm your new pen-pal.

"Today," said Ms Garland, when everyone had had time to read their piece of paper, "we're going to learn how to write letters to our new pen-pals."

A cheer went up in the classroom.

"Now, how many of you have written a letter before?"

One or two of the children waved their hands in the air.

As Ms Garland began to describe what a letter should look like, Shelley, who always sat on her own, took her books and slipped quietly down to the back of the classroom, hoping no one had noticed her.

"The first thing to do," said Ms Garland, "is to write your own address on the top of the page on the right-hand side. That way the person you are writing to will know where you are and will be able to write back. For example, when the President of Ireland writes a letter, the top right-hand corner looks like this."

She took a piece of chalk and wrote on the blackboard:

Áras an Uachtaráin

Phoenix Park

Dublin 8

"Now, can each of you please write your own address in the same way?"

9

Shelley turned over a new page in her copybook and wrote:

Apartment 14
27 Alder Road
Dublin 5

"Very good," said Ms Garland, coming around to make sure everyone had understood. "Now, the next thing to do is to write today's date underneath." Again she turned to the blackboard and wrote:

Monday 5th February

"After that, move down a couple of lines and, this time at the *left-hand* side of the page, write:

Dear ...

and the name of the person you are writing to. Does everyone understand?"

Shelley moved down a few lines, went to the left-hand side of the page and wrote:

Dear Tomi Wong

"Now," said Ms Garland, "beginning on the next line below, you can write just about anything you like. And, when you've finished, I'll collect all the letters and send them for you. All you have to do is make sure you put your pen-pal's name on the envelope. But remember that your new pen-pal doesn't know anything about you, so you might like to tell something about yourself and where you live. All right now, off you go."

At that, all of the other children put their heads down and began to write furiously. Some of them were even concentrating so much that their tongues stuck out of the sides of their mouths.

"Is there anything the matter, Shelley?" asked Ms Garland, coming down to find Shelley staring at the page with nothing written on it except her address, the date and *Dear Tomi Wong*. "It's not like you to run out of ideas."

Shelley looked up sadly. "I don't know what to write, Miss," she said. "My life is so ordinary that no one would want to hear about it. I wish I still lived in the countryside. Something exciting always happened there."

Ms Garland knew that Shelley was not very happy since she had moved to the city with her mother, but she knew that maybe Shelley just needed some encouragement.

"Now, Shelley," she said, "you must try to remember that all lives are full of extraordinary things. It's just that people forget how extraordinary they are because they see them day after day."

Shelley had to think about this for a minute, so Ms Garland continued.

"Imagine that you wrote a letter to someone who knew nothing at all about you or where you lived," she said.

"You mean like Tomi Wong?" said Shelley.

"Yes," said Ms Garland. "Like Tomi Wong. Imagine how exciting that would be."

"But I don't speak Chinese!" said Shelley.

Ms Garland smiled. "That's all right," she said. "Tomi's half-Irish. That's why the first half of his name is in English, more or less. So, what do you think? Will you write to him?"

"I suppose so," said Shelley after a while.

"Excellent," said Ms Garland. "In that case, I'll leave you to it."

Horrid Henry

FRANCESCA SIMON

Henry was horrid.

Everyone said so, even his mother.

Henry threw food, Henry snatched, Henry pushed and shoved and pinched. Even his teddy avoided him when possible.

His parents despaired.

"What are we going to do about that horrid boy?" sighed Mum.

"How did two people as nice as us have such a horrid child?" sighed Dad.

When Horrid Henry's parents took Henry to school they walked behind him and pretended he was not theirs.

Children pointed at Henry and whispered to their parents, "That's Horrid Henry."

"He's the boy who threw my jacket in the mud."

"He's the boy who squashed Billy's beetle."

"He's the boy who …" Fill in whatever terrible deed you like. Horrid Henry was sure to have done it.

Horrid Henry had a younger brother. His name was Perfect Peter.

Perfect Peter always said "please" and "thank you". Perfect Peter loved vegetables. Perfect Peter always used a hankie and never, ever picked his nose.

"Why can't you be perfect like Peter?" said Henry's Mum every day.

As usual, Henry pretended not to hear. He continued melting Peter's crayons on the radiator.

But Horrid Henry started to think.

"What if I were perfect?" thought Henry. "I wonder what would happen."

When Henry woke the next morning, he did not wake Peter by pouring water on Peter's head.

Peter did not scream.

This meant Henry's parents overslept and Henry and Peter were late for Cubs.

Henry was very happy.

Peter was very sad to be late for cubs.

But because he was perfect, Peter did not whine or complain.

On the way to Cubs Henry did not squabble with Peter over who sat in front. He did not pinch Peter and he did not shove Peter.

Back home, when Perfect Peter built a castle, Henry did not knock it down. Instead, Henry sat on the sofa and read a book.

Mum and Dad ran into the room.

"It's awfully quiet in here," said Mum. "Are you being horrid, Henry?"

"No," said Henry.

"Peter, is Henry knocking your castle down?"

Peter longed to say "yes". But that would be a lie.

"No," said Peter.

He wondered why Henry was behaving so strangely.

"What are you doing, Henry?" said Dad.

"Reading a wonderful story about some super mice," said Henry.

Dad had never seen Henry read a book before. He checked to see if a comic was hidden inside.

There was no comic. Henry was actually reading a book.

"Hmmmmn," said Dad.

It was almost time for dinner. Henry was hungry and went into the kitchen where Dad was cooking.

But instead of shouting, "I'm starving! Where's my food?" Henry said, "Dad, you look tired. Can I help get supper ready?"

"Don't be horrid, Henry," said Dad, pouring peas into boiling water. Then he stopped.

"What did you say, Henry?" asked Dad.

"Can *I* help, Dad?" said Perfect Peter.

"I asked if you needed any help," said Henry.

"I asked first," said Peter.

"Henry will just make a mess," said Dad. "Peter, would you peel the carrots while I sit down for a moment?"

"Of course," said Perfect Peter.

Peter washed his spotless hands.

Peter put on his spotless apron.

Peter rolled up his spotless sleeves.

Peter waited for Henry to snatch the peeler. But Henry laid the table instead. Mum came into the kitchen.

"Smells good," she said. "Thank you, darling Peter, for laying the table. What a good boy you are."

Peter did not say anything.

"I laid the table, Mum," said Henry.

Mum stared at him.

"You?" said Mum.

"Me," said Henry.

"Why?" said Mum.

Henry smiled.

14

"To be helpful," he said.

"You've done something horrid, haven't you, Henry?" said Dad.

"No," said Henry. He tried to look sweet.

"I'll lay the table tomorrow," said Perfect Peter.

"Thank you, angel," said Mum.

"Dinner is ready," said Dad.

"You're very quiet tonight, Henry," said Dad.

"The better to enjoy my lovely dinner," said Henry.

"Henry, where are your peas and carrots?" asked Mum.

"I ate them," said Henry. "They were delicious."

Mum looked on the floor. She looked under Henry's chair. She looked under his plate.

"You ate your peas and carrots?" said Mum slowly.

She felt Henry's forehead.

"Are you feeling all right, Henry?"

"Yeah," said Horrid Henry. "I'm fine, thank you for asking," he added quickly.

Mum and Dad looked at each other. What was going on?

Then they looked at Henry.

"Henry, come here and let me give you a big kiss," said Mum. "You are a wonderful boy. Would you like a piece of fudge cake?"

Peter interrupted.

"No cake for me, thank you," said Peter. "I would rather have more vegetables."

Henry let himself be kissed. Oh my, it was hard work being perfect.

He smiled sweetly at Peter.

"I would love some cake, thank you," said Henry.

Perfect Peter could stand it no longer. He picked up his plate and aimed it at Henry. Then Peter threw the spaghetti.

Henry ducked.

SPLAT!

Spaghetti landed on Mum's head. Tomato sauce trickled down her neck and down her new pink fuzzy jumper.

"PETER!!!" yelled Mum and Dad.

"YOU HORRID BOY!" yelled Mum.

"GO TO YOUR ROOM!!" yelled Dad.

Perfect Peter burst into tears and ran to his room.

Mum wiped spaghetti off her face. She looked very funny.

Henry tried not to laugh. He squeezed his lips together tightly.

But it was no use. I am sorry to say that he could not stop a laugh escaping.

"It's not funny!" shouted Dad.

"Go to your room!" shouted Mum.

But Henry didn't care.

Who would have thought being perfect would be such fun?

Things that Go Bump in the Day

TONY ROSS

Foggy was a little ghost, who lived with his Mum and Dad at the top of a spooky old house. Foggy was only born about five hundred years ago, so he was a very young ghost. He had lived in lots of places, including a castle, but this was the best. Ghost families like spooky old places because they make them feel safe. This one had lots of bats and spiders for pets. There were woodlice too, but they make rotten pets. You can't teach them anything, and they are not very playful. Foggy nearly taught a woodlouse to sit up and beg, but it kept falling on its back and kicking its legs in the air.

Foggy loved being a ghost. But sometimes life got a little BORING. There are not many things a ghost can do. Then Foggy found a book of ghost stories and things began to get better. The first story was about a ghost who walked through walls.

"That'll be a FAB thing to do!" said Foggy to a creepy slug. And he walked BONK into a wall. All he did though, was bump his nose.

"Shouldn't believe everything you read," giggled the creepy slug.

The next story was about a ghost who walked all over a house shouting "OOOOOHHH!" and waving his hands in the air, and jumping out of dark places. Foggy thought that was a silly way to behave, but he couldn't get the story out of his mind. There was a whole house beyond the dusty rooms where Foggy lived. Maybe wandering around that going "OOOOOHHH!" would be less boring than teaching woodlice to sit up and beg.

That morning, when it was time to go to sleep, Foggy's Mum gave him a cobweb sandwich and a glass of slime. Then she tucked him into bed.

"Mum," said Foggy, "what's it like in the rest of the house? Are there any dark places?"

Mum kissed Foggy on the bump at the end of his nose.

"Don't you dare go into the rest of the house," she warned. "The rest of the house is a TERRIBLE place. Your Dad went there once, and said it was really scary. He said it was horribly CLEAN, and smelt of SOAP, with sunlight all over the place and lots of knobs on everything. UGH!" she shuddered.

Foggy curled up, and pretended to go to sleep. The rest of the house sounded exciting, just like an adventure in a book.

When he was sure his Mum and Dad were asleep, Foggy got up. He went to the door and, making himself very small, he slithered through the keyhole into the rest of the house.

Foggy floated at the top of some stairs. It was true what Mum had said. The house was horribly light, with a funny smell. "That must be soap," shivered Foggy.

Slowly, he went down the stairs. He hovered in the air a little, because there was tickly furry stuff spread all over the floor. He looked around for a friendly bat, even a woodlouse, but there weren't any. "Even the creepies daren't come into this awful place," he said to himself.

With bated breath, the little ghost floated along the landing. His heart pounded inside him, and he was FAR too frightened to go "OOOOOHHH!" Foggy wasn't a particularly brave ghost, and by now he was getting really scared. The rest of the house wasn't a good place.

Foggy turned to go back the way he'd come. Then he saw it! If he'd had a skin, he'd have jumped right out of it. It was HORRIBLE.

It was very big, and it was lumbering along clutching a small model of itself. It had blue eyes, with hairs all round them, and matted yellow hair hung in twists down its back. Worst of all, when it opened its mouth to snarl, it showed fearsome white fangs. And it smelled of SOAP.

Foggy reeled. Back along the landing he fled, waving his arms in the air, and shouting "OOOOOOHHHH!"; up the stairs, through the keyhole, to where his Mum and Dad sat up in bed, wakened by all the commotion.

"Mum," shouted Foggy. "I'VE SEEN A LITTLE GIRL!"

"Don't be silly," said Mum, cuddling her son. "There's no such thing as little girls."

Anna's Six Wishes

MARGRIT CRUICKSHANK

Anna's First Wish: The Ice Cream Cone

Anna Byrne was doing her homework when a big, black, hairy spider came out from behind her spelling book and walked across the table towards her.

Anna was eight. She lived with her parents, her brother Mark who was fourteen, and her cat Tiptoes who was exactly one year, seven months and three days. Nothing very special ever seemed to happen to Anna, Mark, or even Tiptoes. Nothing very special – until this particular afternoon.

It was hot. Very, very hot. The kind of day when you dream of jumping into a cool, clear swimming pool and long for an ice cream. Anna had read the words in her spelling book from the top to the bottom, from the bottom to the top, and from the top to the bottom again. She had never been so bored.

And then this spider walked out from behind her book.

"Yuck!" Anna said.

She pushed back her chair and grabbed her English copy.

The spider glared at her. "And just what do you think you're doing?" it asked in a squeaky, angry, spidery sort of voice.

Anna guiltily hid the copy behind her back.

"You were just about to squash me into a squidgy black blob," it accused her.

One part of Anna's mind told her that there's nothing wrong with squashing spiders into squidgy

black blobs. Another part told her that spiders don't speak. But, instead of saying any of this, she found herself stuttering, "Oh no, I wasn't!"

"Oh yes, you were!" said the spider. "Just because I'm black and hairy and I crawl. Isn't that right?"

Anna blushed.

"Well, let me tell you, you great, big, lumpy, horrible, white, *human* thing, other spiders find me beautiful. So there!"

Anna let her copy drop on to the chair behind her.

"Well?" the spider asked.

"Well, what?"

"You could at least say you're sorry."

Anna wasn't. Not really. But she muttered "Sorry" all the same.

"That's better," said the spider. "Now that you're beginning to show some manners, I can tell you why I'm here. I'm your fairy-godmother."

"You're *what*?" The only fairy-godmother Anna

21

knew was Cinderella's. And Cinderella's fairy-godmother
was a pretty lady in a fluffy pink dress who wore a
diamond tiara on her head and had wings growing out
of her shoulders. Not a great black hairy spider who
thought that she was beautiful.

"I'm your fairy-godmother," repeated the spider.
"And I'm here to tell you that you can have three wishes."

Anna stared at it. "You have to be kidding," she said.

The spider shrugged its eight shoulders. "Whatever
you say."

If this was a dream, Anna thought, it was a very real
one. "Why only three wishes?" she asked. "If you're that
clever, why not make it ten? Or a hundred? Or a million
billion trillion *squillion* wishes?"

"Oh, all right, then," said the spider. "I'll give you six.
But that's my final offer. And don't go thinking you can
make any of them my-wish-is-to-be-granted-any-wish-I-
like-from-now-until-forever. That's been tried and it
doesn't work."

Anna still didn't believe this was happening to her.
What *would* she wish for, if she really had a fairy-
godmother? "I'd like," she said slowly, "a tape-recorder …
and new shoes … and lunch at MacDonald's …" she
found she was getting the hang of it, "and a trip to the
Zoo and a television of my own and a new bike and a
puppy and a pony and a model aeroplane that flies," she
went on, "and for Granny to come and give me five
pounds and for all my homework to be done for me by
magic and for a digital watch and …"

"That's more than six," interrupted the spider. "Also,
I forgot to tell you: you can't have them all at once. You
only get one at a time. So start again. And this time
think of what you *really* want."

Sunkaissa
the Golden-haired Princess

Michael Rosen

Sunkaissa the Golden-haired Princess is a traditional tale from Nepal. It is retold by Michael Rosen.

Once long ago, in the mountains, a huge and horrible monster fell in love with a golden-haired princess called Sunkaissa. He watched her going about her work and one day, when she was out working, he seized her and took her off to his cave higher up the mountain.

Sunkaissa's family were overcome with despair and sadness that they had lost their beautiful girl.

But her eldest brother was a brave young man and he said, "Listen, we'll never get her back sitting round here crying. I'm going to go up the mountain and find her."

"No," said his father, "the monster has taken her. You're no match for him. He'll tear you apart with one blow. Isn't it bad enough that we've lost a daughter? We don't want to lose a son as well."

But the young man wouldn't listen.

"I can't sit here, knowing that the monster has her in his clutches. I'd rather die than put up with it."

Off he went, up, up the mountain, but there was no sign of his sister. He crossed right over the top down on to the other side; he crossed valleys, rivers, forests, but

23

never a sign of the monster or Sunkaissa. Then one day, he was sitting by a stream when he glanced down and saw, there in the grass, some long golden hairs. Surely these must belong to Sunkaissa, he thought. If I follow the stream I'll find her.

Off he went, following the stream, looking out for signs. Then, glancing up from the ground, he caught sight of a great dark cave in the rocks. He hid behind a tree and watched and waited. It wasn't long before a young woman with long golden hair came out. She sat down on the grass and started combing her hair. It was Sunkaissa. Her brother crept closer to her not wanting to surprise her and make her call out. Just as he was close by, she dropped her comb.

And as she did this, she said, without so much as a glance up at the person who had made a shadow on the ground beside her, "Please pick up my comb for me."

Her brother picked up the comb and handed it to her, but he could see that Sunkaissa didn't know him or recognise him. So he sang to her a song with a tune that they had sung together when they were young:

"I am your brother, one of your own,
I've travelled the mountains to find you,
I've looked in the fields, I've looked by the streams,
And now I've found you, you can come home."

It could have been the words, it could have been the tune – Sunkaissa now recognised her brother. And she was frightened.

"I can't come, dear brother. The monster will catch us and tear us to bits."

"Well, hide me somewhere near so that I can have time to think how we can get rid of the monster."

"You can hide in the cowshed," said Sunkaissa. "In there is a cow. Nothing like one you've ever seen before. Enormous. Gigantic. When she moos, jump into her mouth and hide. Go now, quickly, before the monster comes back."

The brother dashed off to the cowshed and there was the biggest cow the world has ever seen. He climbed up on to a beam and when the cow mooed, he jumped into its mouth. And there he sat till the evening.

Suddenly there came a great shaking of the ground and a great roaring in the air. The door of the cowshed crashed open and there stood the monster.

"I smell the smell of a human being," he roared.

"No," said the cow. "You've got it wrong. There's no human being in here."

"Don't lie to me, cow," said the monster. "When I say there's a human being in here, then there's a human being."

"Well now," said the cow, "I tell you what. I've always wanted to know how many hairs there are on my body. If you could count all the hairs on my body then I might be able to find a human being for you."

"Very well," growled the monster and he started counting. This shouldn't take me long, he thought.

"1, 2, 3 … 234 … 8976 … one million … (the hours were passing, the monster's eyes were beginning to get tired but on he went) … two million … three million, three million and one …"

Just then the cow shivered. A great big shaky shiver and the monster lost his place.

"I don't know where I was!" he shouted.

"Oh really?" said the cow. "I'm so sorry. Don't worry, start again and I'm sure you'll get it right next time."

The monster started again and this time he got to four million and nineteen when the cow gave another great shaky shiver and the monster lost his place again. Well, this went on for hours and hours. Every time the monster got anywhere near counting all the hairs, the cow shivered. Little by little, the monster began to get tired. His head drooped and he started to mutter.

"Three milly, four humble, bendy boo tousled, two humble and bendy tree; three milly, four humble, bendy boo tousled, two humble and bendy floor; three milly, four humble, bendy boo-" and he flopped to the floor fast asleep.

Out of the cow's mouth jumped the brother. He leapt onto the monster and killed him. Then he ran to find Sunkaissa and together they made the long journey home. You can imagine how overjoyed their family and the people of the village were to see them, and how they loved hearing the story of the cow.

And you know, if you watch a cow, you can see to this day that, whether she's in the field or the cowshed, every ten minutes or so she gives a shaky shiver.

THE WHALES' SONG

DYAN SHELDON

Lilly's grandmother told her a story.

"Once upon a time," she said, "the ocean was filled with whales. They were as big as the hills. They were as peaceful as the moon. They were the most wondrous creatures you could ever imagine."

Lilly climbed on to her grandmother's lap.

"I used to sit at the end of the jetty and listen for whales," said Lilly's grandmother. "Sometimes I'd sit there all day and all night. Then all of a sudden I'd see them coming from miles away. They moved through the water as if they were dancing."

"But how did they know you were there, Grandma?" asked Lilly. "How would they find you?"

Lilly's grandmother smiled. "Oh, you had to bring them something special. A perfect shell. Or a beautiful stone. And if they liked you the whales would take your gift and give you something in return."

"What would they give you, Grandma?" asked Lilly. "What did you get from the whales?"

Lilly's grandmother sighed. "Once or twice," she whispered, "once or twice I heard them sing."

Lilly's uncle Frederick stomped into the room.

"You're nothing but a daft old fool!" he snapped. "Whales were important for their meat, and for their bones, and for their blubber. If you have to tell Lilly something, then tell her something useful. Don't fill her head with nonsense. Singing whales indeed!"

"There were whales here millions of years before there were ships, or cities, or even cavemen," continued Lilly's grandmother. "People used to say they were magical."

"People used to eat them and boil them down for oil!" grumbled Lilly's uncle Frederick. And he turned his back and stomped out to the garden.

Lilly dreamt about whales.

In her dreams she saw them, as large as mountains and bluer than the sky. In her dreams she heard them singing, their voices like the wind. In her dreams they leapt from the water and called her name.

Next morning Lilly went down to the ocean. She went where no one fished or swam or sailed their boats. She walked to the end of the old jetty, the water was empty and still. Out of her pocket she took a yellow flower and dropped it into the water.

"This is for you," she called into the air.

Lilly sat at the end of the jetty and waited.

She waited all morning and all afternoon.

Then, as dusk began to fall, Uncle Frederick came down the hill after her. "Enough of this foolishness," he said. "Come on home. I'll not have you dreaming your life away."

That night, Lilly awoke suddenly.

The room was bright with moonlight. She sat up and listened. The house was quiet. Lilly climbed out of

bed and went to the window. She could hear
something in the distance, on the far side of the hill.

She raced outside and down to the shore.
Her heart was pounding as she reached the sea.

There, enormous in the ocean, were the whales.
They leapt and jumped and spun across the moon.
Their singing filled up the night.

Lilly saw her yellow flower dancing on the spray.

Minutes passed, or maybe hours. Suddenly Lilly felt
the breeze rustle her nightdress and the cold nip at
her toes. She shivered and rubbed her eyes. Then it
seemed the ocean was still again and the night black
and silent.

Lilly thought she must have been dreaming. She
stood up and turned for home. Then from far, far away,
on the breath of the wind she heard,

"Lilly!
Lilly!"
The whales were calling her name.

The Troll's Story

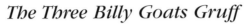

VIVIAN FRENCH

The Three Billy Goats Gruff
is a well-known traditional tale. This story gives
the troll's version of what happened.

Father Troll was warty and ugly and as tall as a church tower. Mother Troll was warty and ugly and as tall as a house. Little Troll was round and hairy and just as tall as you can reach with your hand stretched up high.

On Thursday afternoon Little Troll was wet. He was very wet indeed. As he came stomping in through the open front door he left a trail of water behind him.

"Little Troll!" said Mother Troll. "You're back! Are you all right? How did you get on? Did you do what Father told you?"

"Don't fuss, Mother," said Father Troll. "Of course he did what he was told. Can't you see he's all wet? He's been tossed in the river, just like I was when I was a lad. That's what happens to us trolls, you know. The Great Big Billy Goat Gruff tosses us into the river. It's our very own special story, and now Little Troll can say that he is a real proper troll, just like me. Little Troll, come and give your old dad a hug!"

"ATCHOO!" sneezed Little Troll.

"Dear Little Troll," said Mother Troll, "we'd better get you dry before you catch cold." And she hurried off to fetch the big fluffy towel that was hanging ready by the fire.

Father Troll sat himself down in his big chair. "Tell us all about it," he said.

Little Troll wiped a drip off the end of his nose.

"I was a very good boy," he said, "really I was. I hid under the bridge just exactly like you showed me, Papa."

"Well done, lad," said Father Troll.

"I hope it was the rickety rackety bridge," said Mother Troll and she wrapped Little Troll in the warm towel.

"Oh, it WAS!" said Little Troll. "It was ever so rickety rackety! And I heard the littlest Billy Goat Gruff going patter patter patter –"

"Just a minute!" said Father Troll. "You mean trip trap, trip trap, over the rickety rackety bridge!"

"Oh yes, Papa. He went trip trap, trip trap. And then I jumped out and I said, 'I'm a troll! Fol de rol! And I'll eat you for my dinner!'"

Mother Troll smiled as she rubbed Little Troll dry. "What a clever Little Troll you are!"

Little Troll nodded. "And it was exactly like Papa said it would be. The Little Billy Goat Gruff told me that his brother was going to come over the bridge. He said his brother was bigger and nastier and I should eat him instead."

Father Troll patted Little Troll's head. "Good, good. That's what they always say."

"So, I waited for the Middle-sized Billy Goat Gruff," said Little Troll. "I waited under the rickety rackety bridge, just exactly like you showed me, Papa. And the Middle-sized Billy Goat Gruff came patter patter –"

"No no!" said Father Troll. "You mean trip trap, trip trap!"

"Sorry, Papa. He went trip trap, trip trap, over the rickety rackety bridge. And then I jumped out and I said, 'I'm a troll! Fol de rol! And I'll eat you for my dinner!'"

Mother Troll clapped her hands. "Such a clever little troll!"

"Yes, Mama," said Little Troll. "And then the Middle-sized Billy Goat Gruff told me that his brother was going to come over the bridge. He said his brother was bigger and tastier and I should eat him instead."

Father Troll stamped his feet. "Yes! Yes! That's what they always say!"

"So I waited for the Great Big Billy Goat Gruff," said Little Troll. "I waited under the rickety rackety bridge, and while I was waiting I put my little tiny tippy toe into the water."

"I never told you to do that, Little Troll!" said Father Troll.

"No, Papa. But I did, and the water was oooh! So cold! And then the Great Big Billy Goat Gruff came trip trap, trip trap –"

"You mean tramp tramp tramp!" said Father Troll.

"–He went tramp tramp tramp and then I jumped out and I said, "I'm a troll! Fol de rol! And I'll eat you for my dinner!"

"HURRAH!" cheered Mother and Father Troll together.

"And then," said Little Troll, "that Great Billy Goat Gruff said he wasn't going to be eaten. He said he was going to toss me in the river –"

"AND HE DID!" shouted Mother and Father Troll, and they grabbed each other by the hairy hand and danced round and round Little Troll.

Little Troll stood up.

"NO HE DIDN'T!"

It was very quiet. Mother and Father Troll stared at Little Troll.

"What did you say?" whispered Mother Troll.

"You mean … you ate the Great Big Billy Goat Gruff for your dinner?" whispered Father Troll.

"No!" said Little Troll. "I thought about how cold and wet and nasty the river was. I didn't want to be tossed in, even though Father Troll says all trolls get tossed in the river. I just jumped out of the way and then Great Billy Goat Gruff fell in instead."

There was another silence.

"So … why are you all wet?" asked Mother Troll.

"Oh, the Great Big Billy Goat Gruff couldn't swim," said Little Troll. "So I had to jump in to help him. And he was very *very* pleased and he said he'd never toss any trolls off the rickety rackety bridge ever ever *ever* again." Little Troll unrolled himself from the towel. "Is my tea ready?"

The Winter Hedgehog

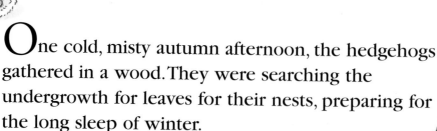

ANN AND REG CARTWRIGHT

One cold, misty autumn afternoon, the hedgehogs gathered in a wood. They were searching the undergrowth for leaves for their nests, preparing for the long sleep of winter.

All, that is, except one.

The smallest hedgehog had overheard two foxes talking about winter.

"What is winter?" he had asked his mother.

"Winter comes when we are asleep," she replied. "It can be beautiful, but it can also be dangerous, cruel and very, very cold. It's not for the likes of us. Now go to sleep."

But the smallest hedgehog couldn't sleep. As evening fell he slipped away to look for winter. When hedgehogs are determined they can move very swiftly, and soon the little hedgehog was far from home. An owl swooped down from high in a tree.

"Hurry home," he called. "It's time for your long sleep." But on and on went the smallest hedgehog until the sky turned dark and the trees were nothing but shadows.

The next morning, the hedgehog awoke to find the countryside covered in fog. "Who goes there?" called a voice, and a large rabbit emerged from the mist, amazed to see a hedgehog about with winter coming on.

"I'm looking for winter," replied the hedgehog. "Can you tell me where it is?"

"Hurry home," said the rabbit. "Winter is on its way and it's no time for hedgehogs."

But the smallest hedgehog wouldn't listen. He was determined to find winter.

Days passed. The little hedgehog found plenty of slugs and insects to eat, but he couldn't find winter anywhere.

Then one day the air turned icy cold. Birds flew home to their roosts and the animals hid in their burrows and warrens. The smallest hedgehog felt very lonely and afraid and wished he was asleep with the other hedgehogs. But it was too late to turn back now!

That night winter came. A frosty wind swept through the grass and blew the last straggling leaves from the trees. In the morning the whole countryside was covered in a carpet of snow.

"Winter!" cried the smallest hedgehog. "I've found it at last." And all the birds flew down from the trees to join him.

The trees were completely bare and the snow sparkled on the grass. The little hedgehog went to the river to drink, but it was frozen. He shivered, shook his prickles and stepped on to the ice. His feet began to slide and the faster he scurried, the faster he sped across it. "Winter is wonderful," he cried. At first he did not see the fox, like a dark shadow, slinking towards him.

"Hello! Come and join me," he called as the fox reached the riverbank. But the fox only heard the rumble of his empty belly. With one leap he pounced on to the ice. When the little hedgehog saw his sly yellow eyes

35

he understood what the fox was about. But every time he tried to run away he slipped on the ice. He curled into a ball and spiked his prickles.

"Ouch!" cried the fox. The sharp prickles stabbed his paws and he reeled towards the centre of the river where he disappeared beneath the thin ice.

"That was close," the smallest hedgehog cried to himself. "Winter is beautiful, but it is also cruel, dangerous and very, very cold."

Winter was everywhere: in the air, in the trees, on the ground and in the hedgerows. Colder and colder it grew until the snow froze under the hedgehog's feet. Then the snow came again and a cruel north wind picked it up and whipped it into a blizzard. The night fell as black as ink and he lost his way. "Winter is dangerous and cruel and very, very cold," moaned the little hedgehog.

Luck saved him. A hare scurrying home gave him shelter in his burrow. By morning the snow was still falling, but gently now, covering everything it touched in a soft white blanket.

The smallest hedgehog was enchanted as he watched the pattern his paws made. Reaching the top of a hill, he rolled into a ball and spun over and over, turning himself into a great white snowball as he went. Down and down he rolled until he reached the feet of two children building a snowman.

"Hey, look at this," said the little girl, "a perfect head for our snowman."

"I'm a hedgehog," he cried. But no one heard his tiny hedgehog voice.

The girl placed the hedgehog snowball on the snowman's body and the boy used a carrot for a nose and pebbles for the eyes. "Let me out," shouted the hedgehog. But the children just stood back and admired their work before going home for lunch.

When the children had gone, the cold and hungry hedgehog nibbled at the carrot nose. As he munched the sun came out and the snow began to melt. He blinked in the bright sunlight, tumbled down the snowman's body and was free.

Time went on. The hedgehog saw the world in its winter cloak. He saw bright red berries disappear from the hedgerows as the birds collected them for their winter larders. And he watched children speed down the hill on their sleighs.

The winter passed. One day the air grew warmer and the river began to flow again. A stoat, who had changed his coat to winter white, changed it back to brown. Then the little hedgehog found crocuses and snowdrops beneath the trees and he knew it was time to go home. Slowly he made his way back to the wood.

From out of every log, sleepy hedgehogs were emerging from their long sleep.

"Where have you been?" they called to the smallest hedgehog.

"I found winter," he replied.

"And what was it like?" asked his mother.

"It was wonderful and beautiful, but it was also …"

"Dangerous, cruel and very, very cold," finished his mother.

But she was answered by a yawn, a sigh and a snore and the smallest hedgehog was fast asleep.

The Toad Tunnel

ANTHONY MASTERS

"STOP! TOADS CROSSING!" Jenny held up the hand-painted sign but the cars didn't slow down at all! They were all driving to the beach and wanted to get to the car park before it was full.

Already, dozens of toads had been squashed flat and Jenny was in tears. Alan and Tom watched miserably. No one paid any attention to their sign. The motorists obviously thought they were just messing about.

"I knew this wouldn't work," said Jenny. She looked at Tom. "Now you'll have to dig out that tunnel."

"I'm not going down there," Tom yelled. He was sure the Giant Slime Slug lived in the tunnel. Tom had dreamt about it last night.

In his dream, Jenny and Alan had forced Tom to struggle through the Toad Tunnel. Halfway through, he found that he was stuck in some horrible sticky slime. It was like crawling through treacle.

Then Tom had heard the soft slithering of the Giant Slime Slug and he saw the black monster heading towards him. It had one eye in the middle of its forehead and its mouth was open, showing its huge green fangs. The Giant Slime Slug had looked very hungry and Tom had woken up screaming.

"I'm not going down the Toad Tunnel," he repeated.

"You've got to!" Alan was furious with him.

"It'll fall in on me," he said miserably. "I'll be trapped."

"Rubbish," said Jenny. "It's made of concrete. It was built specially for the toads to get to their breeding pool. It's just got blocked up with muck, that's all.

38

It needs digging out and you are the only one small enough to do it. If you don't, the toads are going to keep on getting squashed!"

Tom felt guilty. He should help the toads. He wanted to help the toads. But he'd always been scared of small spaces.

Alan, Jenny and Tom Sparks lived in London and were spending a weekend with their grandmother in Sussex. They heard about the Toad Tunnel from her neighbour, Mr Burton. He had helped build the tunnel years ago.

"The toads always head for the breeding pool in March but they've got to get across that road. It's always been busy, so my mate and I built this tunnel under the road. The toads have been using it for years but now it's blocked with mud. Why don't you three have a go at getting the muck out? I'd have a go myself if I wasn't in this wheelchair." Then Mr Burton laughed. "But even if I could get out and about, I'm too big." He glanced at Alan and Jenny. "You wouldn't get in there either. It's only young Tom who stands a chance."

"I'm not going into that tunnel," said Tom. "You know I hate small spaces."

Now Tom stood looking at the dark entrance to the tunnel. He knew he could crawl into it with his seaside spade and get it clear for the toads. But what if he got trapped? What about the Giant Slime Slug?

"What about the toads?" snapped Alan. "They're getting squashed by the minute. Are you going to let them all die?"

"You can't be so selfish!" Jenny accused Tom.

"OK," he said miserably. "I'll do it!"

"You'll be OK, Tom," began Jenny more kindly. "It won't take long."

"Get stuck in!" Alan wasn't in the least sympathetic.

Tom did as he was told, and a few minutes later he had dug out quite a lot of the mud from the entrance.

"Well done!" said Jenny.

"Go for it!" encouraged Alan.

But now the worst was about to happen. He would have to get inside the tunnel.

Tom dug on, inching himself into the pipe, scraping out the mud and throwing it over his shoulder. But it wasn't the mud that he minded. It was what was waiting for him – the Giant Slime Slug.

Then Tom saw something glinting. Was it an eye? He froze, staring in horror at the shining thing in front of him.

"You OK?" yelled Alan. "What are you doing?"

"Keep digging, Tom. You'll soon see daylight. It won't take long," Jenny shouted.

But Tom couldn't hear them. He could only hear the pounding of his own heart as he stared at the winking eye.

He tried to back out of the tunnel but there was too much mud around him.

Then Tom felt something very light tickling his bare, muddy arm. He gave a cry of terror and saw something move. He managed to squeeze to one side and a little light shone up the tunnel.

The toad crawled away from him and then stopped, defeated by the mud wall. It crouched there, pulsating slightly, completely helpless.

Without thinking, Tom started digging again and the toad waited.

The eye was still there in front of them both. Then Tom's spade hit it with a clattering sound.

What an idiot he had been! Tom was gazing at a cola can which had reflected just enough light to fool him. Then, suddenly, he was out on the other side of the road.

The toad crawled out beside Tom and began to waddle down towards the breeding pond.

"Well done," shouted Jenny and Alan. "Well done, Tom!"

But all Tom could do was watch the toad until it got lost in the long grass. He was sure others would follow now that the Toad Tunnel was clear again.

The Stranger from Somewhere in Time

SAM MCBRATNEY

Chapter Two

*Have you ever made a time capsule? Helen and her
friends, Lorna, Bopper, Foxy and Murdo are
preparing one. They arrange to meet in Murdo's
garage after tea. Everybody brings something to put
in the time capsule.*

I arrived in Murdo's garage with a jar of anti-wrinkle
cream borrowed from my Mum, a can of de-icer
borrowed from Dad, and a slinky toy that used to be
able to go down the stairs on its own.

Lorna had brought along sunglasses, a Mickey
Mouse toothbrush, an electric plug and an X-ray of the
bone she'd broken last year. And a red Frisbee.

Foxy Ward produced a tin-opener, a pocket
calculator, a packet of sweetpea seeds, a magnifying
glass and a whistle. Since this whole crazy idea came
from him, he also supplied the time capsule – a white
polystyrene box.

"My turn!" announced Bopper, laying a chewed-up
old shoe on the garage bench, and then a round of
brown bread. Next came a disposable nappy, £400 of
Monopoly money, and a dead daddy-long-legs. Nobody
said a word as Foxy placed that little lot into the time
capsule. We were all speechless.

Now it was Murdo's turn. He'd only managed to
think of two things. One was an oven glove and the

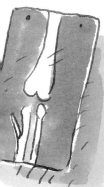

other was a parcel wrapped in bright blue paper.

"That's my birthday present," he said. "It was in the cupboard under the sink. Mum doesn't know I found it. I'm not supposed to have it until next week."

"What's in it?" asked Bopper.

"Dunno, I haven't opened it."

Everyone loves a mystery parcel. I could feel three soft lumps when I took it into my hands. Foxy shook it and Bopper sniffed at it, but Murdo's present didn't rattle or smell.

"Careful! I don't want anything to happen to it," he said.

"It won't," Foxy assured him. "Now, everybody put your names on this computer print-out and we'll seal the whole thing up."

The print-out said:

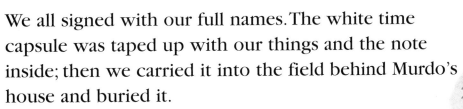

Dear Stranger from Somewhere in Time,

These things were buried here by people at the end of the twentieth century. If you have time travel, come back and visit us. We all live in Mountview Avenue, except Bopper.

Signed:

We all signed with our full names. The white time capsule was taped up with our things and the note inside; then we carried it into the field behind Murdo's house and buried it.

"Right," Foxy said. "We'll come back tomorrow morning at nine thirty and see if he wants to contact us."

"Who?" asked Lorna.

"The Stranger from Somewhere in Time."

"He might be a she," I pointed out. "And how will this Stranger from Somewhere in Time get in touch with us? Can I remind everyone that I'm only leaving my Mum's anti-wrinkle cream here for one night, not ten thousand years!"

"Look," said Foxy, "after ten thousand years they find the capsule, but they come back to our present. We won't know that any time has passed. Understand?"

Of course I didn't understand, but I wasn't going to admit it.

In bed that night I thought that maybe Foxy's words made a weird sort of sense. Perhaps in years to come people would discover how to travel in time. After all, people from the Stone Age would freak out if they saw what we can do nowadays. I tried to zoom my mind forward to the year AD 12000. What would they make of anti-wrinkle cream and a fingerless oven glove? Not to mention a blue mystery parcel and a disposable nappy!

It's Not Fair! ... that I'm little

BEL MOONEY

Kitty was the smallest girl in her class. Usually she did not care. She could swim well, and run as fast as most people – well, almost – and once came first in the egg-and-spoon race on Sports Day. So it did not matter – being small. That was what Kitty thought.

But one day something happened to make her change her mind. It was one of those days when nothing went right.

First of all, there was a new boy in Kitty's class. His name was Tom, and he was very, very tall. Kitty didn't like him very much, because he called her "Shrimp". The whole class was working on a mural in paint and cut-out paper, and on this day Kitty and Tom and two other children were chosen to do special extra work on it.

Kitty was very excited. She loved painting – especially when you could be really messy. That was why she wanted to paint the sky, with lovely big fluffy clouds floating along. But each time she tried Tom laughed at her.

"You can't reach," he said. "You're too small." And he leaned over her head, and did the bit she wanted to do.

At break she found someone had put her jacket on one of the higher pegs she could not reach and she wouldn't ask Tom or anyone to get it down. So she went outside without it and felt cold. Then the playground helper told her off for not wearing a coat.

"I couldn't reach it," said Kitty in a small voice.

"Oh, you're such a dear little thing," said the lady nicely.

Kitty sighed. It really was not fair.

Then it was the games lesson, when the girls had to play netball. They were learning to stop each other getting the ball. You had to dodge quickly, and jump very high. Kitty wasn't very good at that.

Today she was worse than ever. She did not get hold of the ball. All of the other girls had longer arms and legs and it seemed easy for them. Afterwards one of the girls said something that hurt Kitty very much. "No one will want you in their team, Kitty. You're too tiny!"

47

Kitty was very quiet when she got home. Her Mum noticed. At last Kitty broke into tears. "It's not fair that I'm little," she sobbed.

Kitty told her Mum everything. Mum nodded. "It isn't easy. I was small when I was a little girl, and you ask Daniel what they say to him in school."

Surprised, Kitty went to find her big brother to ask him. He made a face. "They sometimes call me Shorty," he said. "But it's very friendly, so I don't mind."

"Are you small too?" asked Kitty.

"Yes. But I'd rather be me than the boy in our class who's so tall and thin they call him Stringy!"

"You see," said Mum, "most people have got something about themselves they would like to change. When you know that, it makes you feel better about yourself."

Kitty thought about that and she made a plan. The next day, at playtime, she made herself feel brave enough to go up to Tom when he was standing on his own.

"Tom, can I ask you something?" she said.

"What, Shrimp?"

"If you had one wish, what would you change about yourself?"

The tall boy looked surprised. Then he went pink and whispered, "My hair. I hate my hair." Kitty looked at it. It was orangey-brown. She thought it was rather nice.

"At my old school they called me Carrots," he said, "and it wasn't fair. But don't tell anyone, will you – Shrimp?"

Kitty said she wouldn't.

Then she found Susie, the big strong girl who had said Kitty was no good at netball, and asked her the same question. Susie frowned and answered quickly.

"My size," she said, "because I feel like an elephant. I'd like to be smaller. I'd like to be like you."

"Like me?" squeaked Kitty, amazed.

Susie nodded.

Kitty looked round the playground at all the children running around. Some tall, some small. Some fat, some thin. Some dark, some fair. Some shy, some bold. Some who could sing, some who could swim. Some dainty, some clumsy…

"We're all different," she said to herself, "and I suppose that's fair!"

The Lion Cub

EILÍS DILLON

Chapter One

*Mark and his sister Catherine are visiting
Dublin Zoo with their parents. They have already
visited the monkey house and the snake house.
Now they are on their way to look at the big cats.*

At the lion house, Mark's mother said, "Let's hurry
through here. They are lovely to look at, but they do
smell awful."

"They can't help it," said Mark. "It's their nature."

"Well, it's my nature not to like it," his mother said.
"One quick run through will do."

It was true that there was a heavy smell in the lion
house. No one wanted to stay there. As they came out,
however, Mark's father met a friend. It was the old lion
keeper, who had been there since Mark's father was a
small boy, and who always recognised his visitors no
matter what age they might happen to be.

"Mr Ward, glad to see you," the keeper said. "These
your family? Want to show them some lion cubs?"

Immediately Mark knew that this was what he most
wanted to see.

"Yes, yes," he said. "Where are they?"

"What's your name?" the keeper asked.

"Mark."

"Then you're the man for lions," said the keeper.
"I don't know why, but Saint Mark is always represented
by a lion. Called my own son Mark, for that reason, though
he turned into an engineer afterwards. This way, please."

50

He opened a door that led into another part of the building, at the back of the lion house. Inside there were more cages, most of them empty. One contained an animal no bigger than a cat, and very like a cat to look at except for its fierce yellow eyes. Its cage was padlocked and had double bars.

"That's a South American wildcat," said the keeper. "He has tetanus in his claws. One scratch from him would finish you. He'll spend six months in that cage and then he won't be dangerous any more."

"What is tetanus?" Catherine asked. She always liked to understand everything.

"Blood poisoning," said the keeper. "He'll grow out of it. This way please."

At the end of the room, in a cage that had no padlock at all, four lion cubs were playing together. They rolled over and over, holding each other's fur in their little teeth and growling ferociously. They were the size of the biggest cat that Mark had ever seen, and that belonged to Billy, the yardman, on the farm at home.

The keeper opened the cage, stepped inside and picked up two of the cubs.

"One each," he said.

Mark took his and held it, stroking its woolly fur from head to tail. The cub began to purr. Mark and Catherine held the two cubs' heads together but they glared at each other and snarled on a high, angry, note, like cats at night. They took them away again.

"Mine likes me," Mark said, when the cub licked his ear.

"He does too," said the keeper. "You have a way with lions, because of your name, I suppose."

"I'll know this one always, wherever I see him," said Mark.

His cub was darker than any of the others and had a dark-brown stripe on the top of his head.

"Come back in a month or so and I'll let you take him for a walk on the leash," the keeper said.

But Mark knew that with the harvest coming on, there would be no more trips to the zoo for a while. His father had said that this was the only time in summer when a farmer could have a little vacation. In the autumn there would be school, and then Christmas. By the time he would see this lion cub again, it would be as big as a calf.

After a while, the keeper took the cubs and put them back into the cage.

"Don't forget to come back," he said to Mark.

"I won't forget," Mark said. "How could I?"

All the time they were spreading out their picnic lunch and eating it, Mark thought of the lion cub. He wanted to go away by himself to think about it, but of course this was not possible. When they had finished everything, his mother said, "Who will take the bag back to the car?"

"I will," Mark said instantly.

It was a big canvas bag that was always used for picnics. It was big enough for two families, which was a good thing when there were visitors. His father gave him the key of the station wagon and Mark started off, swinging the big bag by the handles.

At the lion house he paused. There was no one about. He looked quickly in every direction and then opened the door at the back of the building and slipped inside.

There was no one there either. Only the South American wildcat spat and hissed at him through its double bars.

The cubs were asleep in a warm, woolly heap in a corner of the cage. He opened the cage door and stepped into it. The cubs made no move. He put the bag on the floor of the cage and opened its neck wide. Then he picked up his own cub very carefully and laid it inside. He closed the zip fastener slowly, so as not to disturb the other cubs. None of them moved, nor even opened an eye to see what he was doing.

He left the cage, closing the door quietly, and let himself out of the building. There was still no one around. The cub was heavy in the bag but he carried it high so that it would look rather empty if anyone were to wonder about it.

No one did. He passed through the entrance gates, where the ticket collector said, "Had a good lunch? Feel nice and full?"

"Yes, thank you," said Mark.

He opened the back of the station wagon and put the
bag as near to the door as possible. He pressed the bag
with his hand and thought he felt the cub warm inside.

"No noise on the way home, please," he whispered.
"No growling, no purring."

Then he locked the door again and went back to
find the rest of the family.

The Chicken Gave It to Me

ANNE FINE

Chapter One

Andrew laid it on Gemma's desk. A cloud of farmyard dust puffed up in her face. The first thing she asked when she stopped sneezing was:

"Where did you get that?"

"The chicken gave it to me."

"What chicken? How could a chicken give it to you? It's a *book*."

It was, too. A tiny little book. The cover was just a bit of old farm sack with edges that looked as if they had been – yes, well – *pecked*. And the writing was all thin and scratchy and – there's no way round this – *chickeny*.

"This is ridiculous! Chickens can't write books. Chickens can't *read*."

"The chicken gave it to me." Andrew repeated helplessly.

"But *how*?"

So Andrew told her how he'd been walking past the fence that ran round the farm sheds, and suddenly this chicken had leaped out in front of him in the narrow pathway.

"Pounced on me, really."

"Don't be silly, Andrew. Chickens don't pounce."

"This one did," Andrew said stubbornly. "It fluttered and squawked and made the most tremendous fuss. I was quite frightened. And it kept pushing this book at me with its scabby little foot – just pushing the book towards me whichever way I stepped. The chicken was absolutely determined I should take it."

Gemma sat back in her desk and stared. She stared at Andrew as if she'd never even seen him before, as if they hadn't been sharing a desk for weeks and weeks, borrowing each other's rubbers, getting on one another's nerves, telling each other secrets.
She thought she knew him well. Had he gone mad?

"Have you gone *mad*?"

Andrew leaned closer and hissed rather fiercely in her ear.

"Listen," he said. "I didn't *choose* to do this, you know. I didn't *want* this to happen. I didn't get out of bed this morning and fling back the curtains and say to myself, 'Heigh-ho! What a great day to walk to school down the path by the farm sheds, minding my own business, and get attacked by some ferocious hen who has decided I am the one to read his wonderful book –'"

"Her wonderful book," interrupted Gemma. "Hens aren't him. They're all her. That's how they get to lay eggs."

Andrew chose to ignore this.

"Well," he said. "That's what happened. Believe me or don't believe me. I don't care. I'm simply telling you that this chicken stood there making a giant fuss and kicking up a storm until I reached down to pick up her dusty little book. Then she calmed down and strolled off."

"Not strolled, Andrew," Gemma said. "Chickens don't stroll. She may have strutted off. Or even –"

But Andrew had shoved his round little face right up close to Gemma's, and he was hissing again.

"Gemma! This is *important*. Don't you *see*?"

And, all at once, Gemma believed him. Maybe she'd gone mad too. She didn't know. But she didn't think Andrew was making it up, and she didn't think Andrew was dreaming.

The chicken gave it to him.

She picked it up. More dust puffed out as, carefully, she stretched the sacking cover flat on her desk to read the scratchy chicken writing of the title.

The True Story Of Harrowing Farm

Opening it to the first page, she slid the book until it was exactly halfway between the two of them.

Together they began to read.

The Sea of Tranquillity

MARK HADDON

*On 20th July 1969 Neil Armstrong and
Edwin "Buzz" Aldrin landed on the Moon and walked
across the dusty surface of the Sea of Tranquillity.
History was made.*

Years ago there was a little boy who had the solar system on his wall. Late at night, he'd lie in bed with Rabbit and they'd watch the planets spinning round the sun: Mars, the tiny space-tomato, Saturn, sitting in its Frisbee rings, freezing Pluto, turning slowly in the dark, Jupiter, Uranus, Neptune, Venus, Mercury and Earth.

But of all the weird worlds that whirled across his bedroom wall, his favourite was the moon, a small and bald and ordinary globe of rock that loop-the-looped its way through outer space.

He leant across the windowsill at night and watched the moon slide up into the sky above the biscuit factory.

He borrowed Dad's binoculars and gazed for hours at the empty deserts and the rocky mountains.

And it made him dizzy just to think that he was looking at another world two hundred thousand miles away.

He got an atlas of the moon for Christmas and he read it like a storybook.

He dreamed of going there, of rocketing across the cold, black miles, and landing on the crumbly rock. He dreamed of visiting the craters in the atlas, Prosper Henry, Klaproth, Zack. He dreamed of driving in a fat-tyred moon-mobile, across the Bay of Rainbows and the Sea of Rains …

He kept a scrapbook called *The Journey to the Moon*. Inside were photographs of rockets taking off from Cape Canaveral and astronauts in pumped-up suits and fishbowl helmets, floating in the zero gravity around their little metal rooms.

He borrowed library books and read how astronauts had orbited the earth and walked in space, and how they'd flown around the moon itself. And every night he hoped and hoped that one day they would find a way to land and walk across the tiny world where he had dreamed of walking.

And eventually, one cloudless night, they did.

He couldn't sleep. Midnight had come and gone, but he was wide awake and standing at the window in his dressing gown, because two astronauts were walking on the surface of the moon, two hundred thousand miles above his bedroom.

At 3 a.m. he went downstairs and turned the television on. And there they were, on the flickery screen, bouncing slowly through the dust in the Sea of Tranquility, like giants in slow motion.

He stayed awake all night and went to bed at dawn. The sun was coming up outside his window and the moon was fading fast. He fell asleep and in his dreams he walked with them.

That little boy was me. I'm older now. The solar system wall chart fell to pieces long ago, and Rabbit, who is older too, no longer follows me around but sits beside my desk and watches while I work.

Yet still, on cloudless nights, I sometimes sit beside my bedroom window, staring at that tiny, distant world. I think how cold and dark it is up there. No wind. No clouds. No streams. No sky. Just rocks and dust. I think how nothing ever moves, year after year.

And then I think of those two astronauts, and how the prints they made with their big boots will still be there tonight, tomorrow night and every night for millions of years to come.

Bill's New Frock

Anne Fine

Chapter One

When Bill Simpson woke up on Monday morning, he found he was a girl.

He was still standing staring at himself in the mirror, quite baffled, when his mother swept in.

"Why don't you wear this pretty pink dress?" she said.

"I never wear dresses," Bill burst out.

"I know," his mother said. "It's such a pity."

And, to his astonishment, before he could even begin to argue, she had dropped the dress over his head and zipped up the back. "I'll leave you to do up the shell buttons," she said. "They're a bit fiddly and I'm late for work."

And she swept out, leaving him staring in dismay at the mirror. In it, a girl with his curly red hair and wearing a pretty pink frock with fiddly shell buttons was staring back at him in equal dismay.

"This can't be true," Bill Simpson said to himself. "This cannot be true!"

He stepped out of his bedroom just as his father was rushing past. He, too, was late in getting off to work. Mr Simpson leaned over and planted a kiss on Bill's cheek.

"Bye, Poppet," he said, ruffling Bill's curls. "You look very sweet today. It's not often we see you in a frock, is it?"

He ran down the stairs and out of the house so quickly he didn't see Bill's scowl, or hear what he muttered savagely under his breath.

Bella the cat didn't seem to notice any difference. She purred and rubbed her soft furry body around his ankles in exactly the same way as she always did.

And Bill found himself spooning up his cornflakes as usual. It was as if he couldn't help it. He left the house at the usual time, too. He didn't seem to have any choice. Things, though odd, were just going on in their own way, as in a dream.

Or it could be a nightmare! For hanging about on the corner was the gang of boys from the other school. Bill recognised the one they called Mean Malcolm in his purple studded jacket.

I think I'll go round the long way instead, Bill thought to himself. I don't want to be tripped up in one of their nasty scuffles, like last week, when all the scabs were kicked off my ankle.

Then Bill heard the most piercing whistle.
He looked around to see where the noise was coming from, then realised Mean Malcolm was whistling at him!

Bill Simpson blushed so pink that all his freckles disappeared. He felt so foolish he forgot to turn off at the next corner to go round the long way. He ended up walking right past the gang.

Mean Malcolm just sprawled against the railings, whistling at Bill as he went by wearing his pretty pink frock with shell buttons.

Bill Simpson thought to himself: I'd rather have the scabs kicked off my ankle!

When he reached the main road, there was an elderly woman with curly grey hair already standing on the kerb. To feel safe from the gang, he stood at her side.

"Give me your hand, little girl," she said. "I'll see us both safely across the road."

"No, really," insisted Bill. "I'm fine, honestly. I cross here every day by myself."

The woman simply didn't listen. She just reached down and grasped his wrist, hauling him after her across the road. On the far side, she looked down approvingly as she released him. "That's such a pretty frock!" she said. "You keep it nice and clean."

Rather than say something disagreeable, Bill ran off quickly.

Metalmiss

LINDA PITT

Chapter Six

Mr Grimshaw, the dreaded school inspector, has come to inspect Pinkerton Primary School. The inspector has already had a jug of water spilt on his suit when Mr Jones the headmaster introduces Metalmiss, the school's robot teacher!

Mr Grimshaw turned pale and shrank back against the wall as Metalmiss approached.

"Wha-wha-what's that?" he gasped.

Metalmiss gave him a cold stare.

"I am a robot teacher. Who are you?"

"Gr-Gr-Grimshaw."

"Grimshaw?" Metalmiss paused. Her head swivelled towards Mr Jones. "Is this the Grouchy Grimshaw who was mentioned in the staffroom, Mr Jones?"

"Well … yes … I mean … no …" stuttered Mr Jones helplessly as the school inspector glared at him.

"Is he to join my class?"

"Yes, in a way, but he's a …"

"Very well. Come into my classroom, Grouchy. And no more shouting."

3R watched in amazement as a fat, bespectacled man was led into the room.

"We have a new pupil this afternoon, children. Grouchy Grimshaw."

A giggle went round the classroom but was soon stopped by the robot's steely gaze.

"For the moment, Grouchy, you can sit there, in Rashid's place. He is away today."

Mr Grimshaw sat down beside Harry.

"Now, Grouchy," said Metalmiss, "we have just completed some experiments with water. I will check that you are familiar with these. Harry, will you place the container of water in front of our new pupil?"

"Not water again!" groaned Mr Grimshaw.

"Pupils in 3R do not complain about their lessons, Grouchy. That is something you must learn. Now – when does water become solid?"

"When it freezes, of course," said Mr Grimshaw scornfully.

"Good. Now I will make this water freeze."

"I don't think you'll do that in a hurry," laughed Mr Grimshaw, stirring the water with his finger. He wondered why he had ever felt frightened of this silly robot.

"Take your finger out," hissed Harry.

"Remove your finger from the water, Grouchy," ordered Metalmiss.

"Why?" Mr Grimshaw stirred more wildly. "Why should I?"

Metalmiss pointed at the water. The grey steel of her finger slowly changed to a brilliant, dazzling blue.

Harry grabbed Mr Grimshaw's hand and pulled it clear, just in time.

The water in the container was now a solid block of ice. Mr Grimshaw turned pale as he stared from his finger to the ice and back again.

"Is ice heavier or lighter than water, Grouchy?"

"Heavier," said Mr Grimshaw faintly. He was still recovering from his chilling experience.

Holly raised her hand. "It's lighter, Metalmiss, like an iceberg."

"Good, Holly. That is correct."

Harry began to feel sorry for Mr Grimshaw.

Metalmiss broke off a chunk of ice and they watched it float in a glass of water.

"I meant lighter," growled Mr Grimshaw.

"Then you must say what you mean, Grouchy. But do not worry. You will soon catch up with the other children in 3R."

This was too much for Mr Grimshaw. He leapt to his feet.

"I am not a child!" he shouted. "I will not be treated like a child!"

"Sit down at once, Grouchy."

The robot's eyes were as cold as the ice in the glass. Mr Grimshaw sat down.

"You say that you are not a child. You are not a teacher. You are not a parent. What are you?"

"I am a School Inspector."

"An inspector. I have not been programmed for that. Please wait."

Metalmiss walked to the back of the room. Then she turned, pressed a small red button on the side of her left wrist, and pointed her left forefinger at the screen. Words beginning with "I" slid rapidly across the screen and then halted.

"Here it is … 'inspect' … 'inspector' … 'one who inspects; official employed to supervise a service and make reports'."

"That's it!" cried Mr Grimshaw triumphantly. "I inspect schools and write reports. And what a report I'm going to write about this school!"

Metalmiss walked slowly back to the front of the classroom, turned round and stared at him.

"Will your report be a good one, Inspector?"

Mr Grimshaw's smile of triumph faded as his eyes met the robot's steely gaze.

"Er … yes," he mumbled.

On the robot's cap a row of blue discs began to revolve, slowly at first, then faster. The children nudged each other. They knew what was coming.

Even so, they gasped as the blue rays suddenly shot out and formed a halo above Mr Grimshaw's head.

"You are sure, Inspector?"

"Yes."

The halo changed to purple, to grey, to black.

"It's a lie detector," Harry whispered.

"You are still sure that it will be a good report?"

"No!" screamed Mr Grimshaw, knocking his chair over as he jumped to his feet. "I am going to write a VERY BAD REPORT!"

The halo disappeared.

"In fact," Mr Grimshaw continued viciously, "it will be the worst report that I have ever written. Sloppy school – sloppy teachers – and just wait until I tell Head Office about you, Metalmiss!"

"Sit down," Metalmiss commanded.

For a moment Mr Grimshaw stared back defiantly. Then he shrugged, picked up his chair and sat down. He could wait.

Metalmiss turned to the class.

"And now, 3R, before you go to your music lesson I will read some of our story."

The story was about sailing ships and islands full of buried treasure. The robot's voice seemed softer, less metallic. On her tunic discs spun, glowed, changed colour.

As he listened, Mr Grimshaw removed his glasses and began to breathe deeply. His face, usually so bad-tempered, grew softer, almost dreamy. He sat in a blur of colour, listening to the slow, clear voice. It was like a dream, he thought, the sort of dream that you want to go on for ever and ever.

The story ended. Quietly, the children went off to their music lesson. Mr Grimshaw sat on.

"Did you like our story, Inspector?"

Mr Grimshaw blinked, fumbled for his glasses and put them on. He beamed at Metalmiss.

"It was wonderful – just wonderful. I can't find words to describe it."

"But you will find words for your report, Inspector?"

"Yes, but now I will have to find new words, Metalmiss. It will be my first good report – a very good report."

Stone Fox

JOHN REYNOLDS GARDINER

Chapter One: Grandfather

One day Grandfather wouldn't get out of bed. He just lay there and stared at the ceiling and looked sad.

At first little Willy thought he was playing.

Little Willy lived with his grandfather on a small potato farm in Wyoming. It was hard work living on a potato farm, but it was also a lot of fun. Especially when Grandfather felt like playing.

Like the time Grandfather dressed up as the scarecrow out in the garden. It took little Willy an hour to catch on. Boy, did they laugh. Grandfather laughed so hard he cried. And when he cried his beard filled up with tears.

Grandfather always got up real early in the morning. So early that it was still dark outside. He would make a fire. Then he would make breakfast and call little Willy. "Hurry up or you'll be eating with the chickens," he would say. Then he would throw his head back and laugh.

Once little Willy went back to sleep. When he woke up, he found his plate out in the chicken coop. It was picked clean. He never slept late again after that.

That is … until this morning. For some reason Grandfather had forgotten to call him. That's when little Willy discovered that Grandfather was still in bed. There could be only one explanation. Grandfather was playing. It was another trick.

Or was it?

"Get up, Grandfather," little Willy said. "I don't want to play anymore."

But Grandfather didn't answer.

Little Willy ran out of the house.

A dog was sleeping on the front porch. "Come on, Searchlight!" little Willy cried out. The dog jumped to its feet and together they ran off down the road.

Searchlight was a big black dog. She had a white spot on her forehead the size of a silver dollar. She was an old dog – actually born on the same day as little Willy, which was over ten years ago.

A mile down the road they came to a small log cabin surrounded by tall trees. Doc Smith was sitting in a rocking chair under one of the trees, reading a book.

"Doc Smith," little Willy called out. He was out of breath. "Come quick."

"What seems to be the matter, Willy?" the doctor asked, continuing to read.

Doc Smith had snow white hair and wore a long black dress. Her skin was tan and her face was covered in wrinkles.

"Grandfather won't answer me," little Willy said.

"Probably just another trick," Doc Smith replied. "Nothing to worry about."

"But he's still in bed."

Doc Smith turned a page and continued to read. "How late did you two stay up last night?"

"We went to bed early, real early. No singing or music or anything."

Doc Smith stopped reading.

"Your grandfather went to bed without playing his harmonica?" she asked.

Little Willy nodded.

Doc Smith shut her book and stood up. "Hitch up Rex for me, Willy," she said. "I'll get my bag."

Rex was Doc Smith's horse. He was a handsome palomino. Little Willy hitched Rex to the wagon, and then they rode back to Grandfather's farm. Searchlight ran on ahead, leading the way and barking. Searchlight enjoyed a good run.

Grandfather was just the same. He hadn't moved.

Searchlight put her big front paw up on the bed and rested her head on Grandfather's chest. She licked his beard, which was full of tears.

Doc Smith proceeded to examine Grandfather. She used just about everything in her little black bag.

"What's that for?" little Willy asked. "What are you doing now?"

"Must you ask so many questions?" Doc Smith said.

"Grandfather says it's good to ask questions."

Doc Smith pulled a long silver object from her doctor's bag.

"What's that for?" little Willy asked.

"Hush!"

"Yes, ma'am. I'm sorry."

When Doc Smith had finished her examination, she put everything back into her little bag. Then she walked over to the window and looked out at the field of potatoes.

After a moment she asked, "How's the crop this year, Willy?"

"Grandfather says it's the best ever."

Doc Smith rubbed her wrinkled face.

"What's wrong with him?" little Willy asked.

"Do you owe anybody money?" she asked.

"No!" little Willy answered. "What's wrong? Why won't you tell me what's wrong?"

"That's just it," she said. "There is nothing wrong with him."

"You mean he's not sick?"

"Medically, he's as healthy as an ox. Could live to be a hundred if he wanted to."

"I don't understand," little Willy said.

Doc Smith took a deep breath. And then she began, "It happens when a person gives up. Gives up on life. For whatever reason. Starts up here in the mind first; then it spreads to the body. It's a real sickness, all right. And there's no cure except in the person's own mind. I'm sorry, child, but it appears that your grandfather just doesn't want to live anymore."

Little Willy was silent for a long time before he spoke. "But what about … fishing … and the Rodeo … and turkey dinners? Doesn't he want to do those things anymore?"

Grandfather shut his eyes and tears rolled down his cheeks and disappeared into his beard.

"I'm sure he does," Doc Smith said, putting her arm around little Willy. "It must be something else."

Little Willy stared at the floor. "I'll find out. I'll find out what's wrong and make it better. You'll see I'll make Grandfather want to live again."

And Searchlight barked loudly.

Bookcase

Poetry

Contents • Poetry

I Have a Lion

KARLA KUSKIN

I had a cat,
Gray
Soft
Fat
Given to grrrring
Quite softly
And prrrrring.
Slipped off one morning
Near the green glen.
That was my cat
Who was not seen again.

I had a dog,
Noisy and yellow
Very cold nose
Wonderful fellow.
Trotted one evening
Out after a pack
Of dog-footed friends
And never came back.

I had a bird,
Bright blue in a cage
Sang without cause
On his miniature stage.
Sat on my shoulder
Looked in my eye.
Sailed out the window
And into the sky.

I have a lion,
Furry and kind
Sits on a shelf
Near the autos that wind.
Eyes wild and golden
Tail like a tuft
He never will slip out and leave me.
He's stuffed.

77

Monday Morning

JOHN C. HEAD

Moaning, groaning,
mumbling, grumbling,
glowering, showering,
rubbing, scrubbing,
washing, sploshing,
groping, soaping,
howling, towelling,
splashing, dashing,
muttering, buttering,
crunching, munching,
sighing, tying,
brushing, rushing,
cramming, slamming
and off to
school.

Breakfast Time

JAMES STEPHENS

The sun is always in the sky
Whenever I get out of bed,
And I often wonder why
It's never late. My sister said

She didn't know who did the trick,
And that she didn't care a bit,
And I should eat my porridge quick.
– I think its mother wakens it.

The Engine Driver

CLIVE SANSOM

The train goes running along the line,
Jicketty-can, jicketty-can.
I wish it were mine, I wish it were mine,
Jicketty-can, jicketty-can.
The engine driver stands in front,
He makes it run, he makes it shunt;

Out of the town,
Out of the town,
Over the hill,
Over the down,
Under the bridges,
Across the lea,
Over the ridge
And down to the sea,
With a jicketty-can, jicketty-can,
Jicketty-jicketty-jicketty-can,
Jicketty-can, jicketty-can.

A Dog's Life

Brian Patten

Sigh, sob,
　　　gulp, bark, gush,
I'm soggy, swampy,
　　　saturated,
bathtime's something
　　　I've always hated!
I'm bedewed,
　　　bedabbled, water-logged,
my ears are frothy,
　　　my dose is clogged,
I might grow fungus!
　　　I might rust!
Bathing a dog
　　　is most unjust!

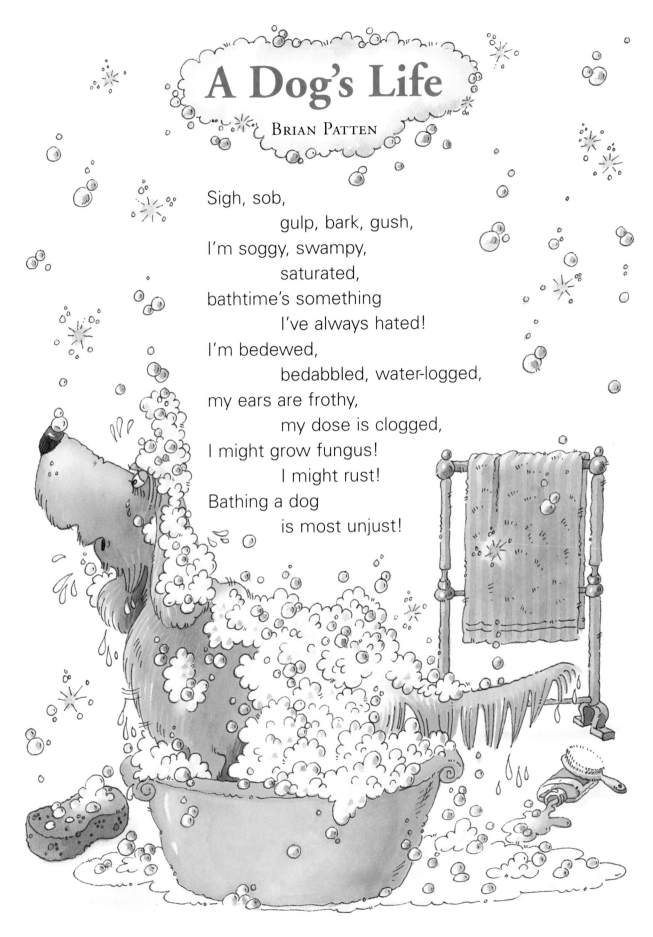

Picking Teams

ALLAN AHLBERG

When we pick teams in the playground,
Whatever the game might be,
There's always somebody left till last
And usually it's me.

I stand there looking hopeful
And tapping myself on the chest,
But the captains pick the others first,
Starting, of course, with the best.

Maybe if teams were sometimes picked
Starting with the worst,
Once in his life a boy like me
Could end up being first!

The Leader

Roger McGough

I wanna be the leader
I wanna be the leader
Can I be the leader?
Can I? I can?
Promise? Promise?
Yippee, I'm the leader
I'm the leader

OK what shall we do?

Allosaurus

JACK PRELUTSKY

Allosaurus liked to bite,
its teeth were sharp as sabres,
it frequently, with great delight,
made mincemeat of its neighbours.

Allosaurus liked to hunt,
and when it caught its quarry,
it tore it open, back and front,
and never said, "I'm sorry!"

Allosaurus liked to eat,
and using teeth and talons,
it stuffed itself with tons of meat,
and guzzled blood by gallons.

Allosaurus liked to munch,
and kept from growing thinner
by gnawing an enormous lunch,
then rushing off to dinner.

Tyrannosaurus

JACK PRELUTSKY

Tyrannosaurus was a beast
that had no friends, to say the least.
It ruled the ancient out-of-doors,
and slaughtered other dinosaurs.

Some One

WALTER DE LA MARE

Some one came knocking
At my wee, small door;
Some one came knocking,
I'm sure – sure – sure;

I listened, I opened,
I looked to left and right,
But nought there was a-stirring
In the still dark night;

Only the busy beetle
Tap-tapping in the wall,
Only from the forest
The screech-owl's call,

Only the cricket whistling
While the dewdrops fall,
So I know not who came knocking,
At all, at all, at all.

Spaghetti

Shel Silverstein

Spaghetti, spaghetti, all over the place,
Up to my elbows — up to my face,
Over the carpet and under the chairs,
Into the hammock and wound round the stairs,
Filling the bathtub and covering the desk,
Making the sofa a mad mushy mess.

The party is ruined, I'm terribly worried,
The guests have all left (unless they're all buried).
I told them, "Bring presents," I said, "Throw confetti."
I guess they heard wrong
'Cause they all threw spaghetti!

Windy Nights

ROBERT LOUIS STEVENSON

Whenever the moon and stars are set,
Whenever the wind is high,
All night long in the dark and wet,
A man goes riding by.
Late in the night when the fires are out,
Why does he gallop and gallop about?

Whenever the trees are crying aloud,
And ships are tossed at sea,
By, on the highway, low and loud,
By at the gallop goes he.
By at the gallop he goes, and then
By he comes back at the gallop again.

The Little Donkey

ELIZABETH SHANE

I saw a donkey
One day old,
His head was too big
For his neck to hold.

His legs were shaky
And long and loose,
They rocked and staggered
And weren't much use.

He tried to gambol
And frisk a bit,
But he wasn't sure
Of the trick of it.

His queer little coat
Was soft and grey,
And curled at his neck
In a lovely way.

His face was wistful,
And left no doubt
That he felt life needed
Some thinking out.

Scissors

ALLAN AHLBERG

Nobody leave the room.
Everyone listen to me.
We had ten pairs of scissors
At half-past two,
And now there's only three.

Seven pairs of scissors
Disappeared from sight.
Not one of you leaves
Till we find them.
We can stop here all night!

Scissors don't lose themselves,
Melt away or explode.
Scissors have not got
Legs of their own
To go running off up the road.

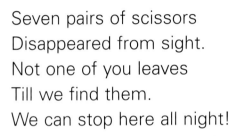

We really need those scissors,
That's what makes me mad.
If it was seven pairs
Of children we'd lost,
It wouldn't be so bad.

I don't want to hear excuses.
Don't anyone speak.
Just ransack this room
Till we find them,
Or we'll stop here … all week!

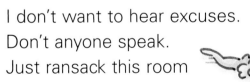

89

The Whale's Hymn

BRIAN PATTEN

In an ocean before cold dawn broke
Covered by an overcoat
I lay awake in a boat
And heard a whale.

Hearing a song so solemn and so calm
It seemed absurd to feel alarm –
But I had a notion it sang
God's favourite hymn,

And spoke direct to Him.

GRANDAD

Kit Wright

*Grandad's dead
And I'm sorry about that.*

He'd a huge black overcoat.
He felt proud in it.
You could have hidden
A football crowd in it.
Far too big –
It was a lousy fit
But Grandad didn't
Mind a bit.
He wore it all winter
With a squashed black hat.

*Now he's dead
And I'm sorry about that.*

He'd got twelve stories.
I'd heard every one of them
Hundreds of times
But that was the fun of them:
You knew what was coming
So you could join in.
He'd got big hands
And brown, grooved skin
And when he laughed
It knocked you flat.

*Now he's dead
And I'm sorry about that.*

The Sound Collector

ROGER MCGOUGH

A stranger called this morning
Dressed all in black and grey
Put every sound into a bag
And carried them away

The whistling of the kettle
The turning of the lock
The purring of the kitten
The ticking of the clock

The popping of the toaster
The crunching of the flakes
When you spread the marmalade
The scraping noise it makes

The hissing of the frying-pan
The ticking of the grill
The bubbling of the bathtub
As it starts to fill

The drumming of the raindrops
On the window-pane
When you do the washing-up
The gurgle of the drain

The crying of the baby
The squeaking of the chair
The swishing of the curtain
The creaking of the stair

A stranger called this morning
He didn't leave his name
Left us only silence
Life will never be the same.

I Meant to Do My Work Today

RICHARD LeGALLIENNE

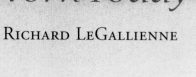

I meant to do my work today –
But a brown bird sang in the apple tree,
And a butterfly flitted across the field,
And all the leaves were calling me.

And the wind went sighing over the land
Tossing the grasses to and fro,
And a rainbow held out its shining hand –
So what could I do but laugh and go?

Daddy fell into the Pond

ALFRED NOYES

Everyone grumbled. The sky was grey.
We had nothing to do and nothing to say.
We were nearing the end of a dismal day.
And there seemed to be nothing beyond,
> Then
>> *Daddy fell into the pond!*

And everyone's face grew merry and bright,
And Timothy danced for sheer delight.
"Give me the camera, quick, oh quick!
He's crawling out of the duckweed!" Click!

Then the gardener suddenly slapped his knee,
And doubled up, shaking silently,
And the ducks all quacked as if they were daft,
And it sounded as if the old drake laughed.
Oh, there wasn't a thing that didn't respond
> *When*
>> *Daddy fell into the pond!*

Gran, Can You Rap?

JACK OUSBEY

Gran was in her chair she was taking a nap
When I tapped her on the shoulder to see if she could rap.
Gran, can you rap? Can you rap? Can you, Gran?
And she opened one eye and said to me, man,
I'm the best rapping Gran this world's ever seen
I'm a tip-top, slip-slap, rap-rap queen.

And she rose from her chair in the corner of the room
And she started to rap with a bim-bam-boom,
And she rolled up her eyes and she rolled round her head
And as she rolled by this is what she said,
I'm the best rapping Gran this world's ever seen
I'm a nip-nap, yip-yap, rap-rap queen.

Then she rapped past my dad and she rapped past my mother,
She rapped past me and my little brother.
She rapped her arms narrow she rapped her arms wide,
She rapped through the door and she rapped outside.
She's the best rapping Gran this world's ever seen
She's a drip-drop, trip-trap, rap-rap queen.

She rapped down the garden she rapped down the street,
The neighbours all cheered and they tapped their feet.
She rapped through the traffic lights as they turned red
As she rapped round the corner this is what she said,
I'm the best rapping Gran the world's ever seen,
I'm a flip-flop, hip-hop, rap-rap queen.

She rapped down the lane she rapped up the hill,
And as she disappeared she was rapping still.
I could hear Gran's voice saying, Listen, man,
Listen to the rapping of the rap-rap Gran.
I'm the best rapping Gran this world's ever seen
I'm a –
Tip-top, slip-slap,
Nip-nap, yip-yap,
Hip-hop, trip-trap,
Touch yer cap,
Take a nap,
Happy, happy, happy, happy,
Rap-rap-queen.

Winter Morning

Ogden Nash

Winter is the king of showmen,
Turning tree stumps into snowmen
And houses into birthday cakes
And spreading sugar over the lakes.
Smooth and clean and frost white
The world looks good enough to bite.
That's the season to be young,
Catching snowflakes on your tongue.

Snow is snowy when it's snowing
I'm sorry it's slushy when it's going.

To a Squirrel
at Kyle-Na-No

W. B. YEATS

Come play with me;
Why should you run
Through the shaking tree
As though I'd a gun
To strike you dead?
When all I would do –
Is to scratch your head
And let you go.

Kite

JUNE CREBBIN

I'm
part of a
project on flight.
I'm supposed to attain
a great height. But
unfortunately
I got stuck
in a tree
so
it
looks
like
I'm
here
for
the
night!

BOOKCASE

Plays

Contents • Plays

Real Dragons Roar

Jacquie Buttriss and Ann Callander

CAST	Narrator	Dragon
	Prince	Anna
	Guard	Farmer

Narrator Long ago, in a far away kingdom, there lived a dragon. But he wasn't an ordinary dragon. He was a very friendly dragon. He didn't breathe fire when strangers walked past his cave.

Dragon I don't even smoke.

Narrator He wore a pair of brightly coloured socks which he pulled right up to his scaly knees.

Dragon I don't want my sharp claws to hurt anybody.

Narrator And he never roared.

Dragon *(covering his ears)* I hate loud noises.

Narrator The dragon liked a quiet life. Best of all he liked reading books and eating fudge.

Dragon Especially both at once!

Narrator The dragon had many friends but his best friends were a farmer and his clever daughter, Anna.

Dragon She makes really good fudge.

Narrator Now, in the same kingdom, there was a very selfish prince who lived in a castle.

Prince   I don't see why I should have to share things with anyone. After all, I am a prince. The trouble is I'm bored. No one will play with me.

Guard   I'll play a game with you, Your Highness.

Prince   Oh, all right. Go and get the snakes and ladders.

Narrator   The guard went away and the prince stared out of the castle window.

Prince   *(looking fed up)* It's hopeless playing games with the guard. He gets everything wrong.

Narrator   Just then, the guard came back carrying a small ladder.

Guard   I couldn't find any snakes but I've found this ladder, Your Highness.

Prince   Oh no! Not that kind of ladder. I want the game of snakes and ladders.

Guard	I'm sorry, Your Highness. I'll go and look again.
Prince	No, don't bother. We'll play hide and seek instead.
Guard	Yes, Your Highness. I like hide and seek.
Prince	I'll go and hide, because I know all the best places. You count to 100.
Guard	But I can only count to 29, Your Highness.
Prince	Well, count to 29 very slowly.
Narrator	The guard began counting very slowly, while the prince ran off to hide.
Guard	18 … 19 … 20 … 29 … coming!
Narrator	Meanwhile, the farmer and his daughter were planning to visit the dragon.
Farmer	Let's take the dragon some books to read and a basket of food.
Anna	I've made him some fudge too.
Narrator	So they set off to visit their friend, the dragon, but when they got to his cave, they found the dragon looking miserable.
Farmer	*(looking concerned)* What's the matter?
Anna	Aren't you well? I've brought you some fudge.
Dragon	Thank you.
Narrator	The dragon gave a big sigh and popped a piece of fudge in his mouth.
Farmer	Tell us why you are so sad.
Dragon	It was that book.

Farmer	What book?
Dragon	The one you gave me about St George.
Anna	Didn't you like it? I thought you might like to read about another dragon.
Dragon	Yes. But St George rescued a maiden in distress and killed the dragon.
Farmer	Oh, don't worry. Nobody kills dragons nowadays.
Anna	Especially friendly dragons like you.
Dragon	Why is it always the knight who rescues the maiden in distress? Why can't a dragon rescue a maiden?
Farmer	I'm sure you could, but there aren't many maidens in distress around any more.
Anna	Thank goodness!
Dragon	But I want to do something exciting, and be famous. I want to be a hero.
Narrator	He popped another piece of fudge in his mouth and a big tear rolled slowly down his scaly cheek.
Anna	Don't worry, Dragon. I'll go and pick some flowers to cheer you up.
Narrator	Meanwhile, back at the castle, the prince was bored. The guard came back.
Prince	What's the good of playing hide and seek if you don't come looking for me?
Guard	Oh, I forgot I was looking for you and I went off to hide.

Prince	You're no good at hide and seek. Oh, what can I do now?
Guard	We could play another game.
Prince	But you get them all wrong. No, I've got a better idea. Let's go for a ride and we can look for someone who is good at playing games.
Guard	Yes, Your Highness.
Prince	Go and tell the groom to saddle two horses.
Guard	At once, Your Highness.
Narrator	The prince and the guard rode towards the village. They saw Anna picking some flowers.

Prince	*(pointing to Anna)* There's a girl over there. Perhaps she knows how to play games. Quick, go and talk to her.
Guard	What shall I say?
Prince	… um, you could ask her what time it is.
Guard	But we already know what time it is. My tummy's rumbling. It's tea time.
Prince	Never mind. I'll speak to her myself.
Narrator	The prince rode up to Anna.
Prince	Can you help us?
Anna	What is the matter?
Prince	My guard and I are looking for someone.
Anna	Who?
Prince	Someone who can play games better than anyone else in the kingdom.
Anna	What kind of games?
Prince	Well, I am particularly good at chess. Do you know anyone who plays chess?
Anna	Yes, me! I like playing chess.
Prince	Then I challenge you to a match at the castle.
Anna	All right. But I must tell my father first.
Prince	No. It's getting late. We must go now.
Anna	But … but …
Prince	Guard. Seize this girl. Bring her back to the castle.
Guard	Yes, Your Highness.

Anna	Let me go. Help! *(loudly)*
Narrator	Inside the cottage, Anna's father heard Anna shouting. He rushed outside.
Farmer	Hey! What's happening? What are you doing with my daughter? Where are you taking her?
Narrator	The prince and the guard did not answer. They were already riding away towards the castle with Anna.
Farmer	Oh, what shall I do?
Narrator	The farmer thought hard and decided to go and see his friend, the dragon. The dragon was sitting in his cave darning his spare socks.
Farmer	You must help Anna. The prince and the guard have taken her away to the castle.
Dragon	That's dreadful. But what can I do?
Farmer	You can rescue her.
Dragon	Who, me?
Farmer	Yes. You are the only one who can help her.
Dragon	You mean she's a maiden in distress?
Farmer	Yes.
Narrator	The dragon was delighted. Here was his big chance to be a hero.
Dragon	But … how?
Farmer	Here, I've brought a book about dragons. Perhaps that will give us some good ideas.
Dragon	I hope so!

Narrator They looked at the dragon book together and read about all the things that a dragon can do.

Farmer It says here that you can terrify people with your sharp claws.

Dragon *(taking off his socks)* Can I really? I'd better take off my socks and see what I can do.

Farmer My goodness! Your claws are frightening!

Dragon What else can I do?

Farmer You can roar so loudly that people will run and hide.

Narrator The dragon opened his mouth and gave a great roar. The farmer was so frightened he ran to hide behind a tree.

Dragon Come back here! I'm just starting to enjoy myself. What else does it say in the book?

Farmer It says here that you can breathe flames.

Narrator The dragon took a deep breath and blew such enormous flames that they burnt the grass outside his cave. He was so surprised that he nearly fell over!

Dragon	Wow! I didn't know I could do that!
Farmer	Well done. You never know what you can do until you try.
Dragon	That's what my teacher used to tell me at dragon school. But I never believed her!
Farmer	Come on then. Now we must go and rescue Anna.
Dragon	I think I'd better have a piece of fudge first.
Narrator	The dragon and the farmer set off together for the castle. They walked up to the huge castle door.
Farmer	How shall we get through this thick wooden door?
Dragon	Don't worry. I'll burn it down. Just watch!
Narrator	The dragon blew with all his might and the door disappeared in a burst of flames.
Farmer	Well done!
Narrator	Then the guard began to shoot arrows at the dragon. But the dragon roared so loudly ...
Dragon	ROAR!
Narrator	... that the guard ran away to hide.
Guard	*(running away)* Help!
Farmer	Look. Here comes the prince with a huge silver sword.
Prince	You might frighten the guard, but you don't frighten me!
Narrator	The dragon's knees trembled.

Dragon *(popping a piece of fudge in his mouth)* I think I'd better have another piece of fudge.

Narrator Then the dragon remembered he was a fierce dragon and he showed his sharp claws and he roared loudly …

Dragon R-O-A-R!

Prince You d-d-d-don't frighten me.

Narrator Then he blew fiery flames at the prince. The prince's coat caught fire.

Prince Help! Help! *(loudly)*

Narrator The guard heard the prince's cries and ran over to the well. He filled a bucket of water and threw it over the prince.

Prince Thank you, Guard. What a clever thing to do. You saved my life.

Narrator Meanwhile, the dragon and the farmer rushed into the castle to look for Anna. She was sitting in a velvet chair and looking down at a chess board.

Farmer	Anna!
Anna	Shhhh! I'm trying to concentrate.
Dragon	Anna! I've come to save you.
Anna	Oh, Dragon. Don't be so old-fashioned. Can't you see I can look after myself?
Dragon	But I roared a terrible roar and showed my sharp claws and I blew fiery flames at the prince.
Anna	I wondered what all the noise was about. But now be sensible and put your socks back on. The prince and I are in the middle of a game of chess.
Narrator	From that day on, the prince and Anna became very good friends. The prince forgot all about being selfish and he started to be kind instead.
Dragon	The guard and I are very good friends too.
Guard	Yes, and the dragon always shares his fudge with me.
Narrator	So, Anna, the prince, the dragon, the guard and the farmer all lived happily ever after.
Anna	If you believe that you'll believe anything.

The Magic Sticks

ROBINA BECKLES WILLSON

CAST   **Narrator**   **Guard**
          Jaspal   **Sita**
          King   **Judge**

Narrator   Long ago, there was a King who lived in India. Every morning he sat on a throne in his golden palace and people came to ask him for advice. One day, a judge came to ask the King for help.

Guard   The judge is here to see you, Your Highness.

Judge   Your Highness, you are known to be the wisest King in India. I have come to ask for your help with a most difficult case in my law court.

King   I will do what I can. Tell me more.

Judge	Two women have been accused of stealing jewels from their mistress, but they both say they did not do it.
King	Then it is quite simple. You need to find out who is telling the truth.
Judge	That is not easy, Your Highness. They both talk so much and tell such good stories, I don't know who to believe.
King	Then how can I help?
Judge	Please would you ask them some questions for me?
King	I will see what I can do. Where are the women now? What are their names?
Judge	They are at the law court, and they are called Jaspal and Sita.
King	Then I shall send an elephant to bring them here. Guard?
Guard	Yes, Your Highness.
King	Take my elephant and bring back Jaspal and Sita.
Guard	Yes, Your Highness. I will bring them with all speed.
Narrator	Soon the two women arrive at the palace and come in to the King's throne room.
Guard	Here are Jaspal and Sita, Your Highness.
King	Thank you, Guard. Wait here. I may need you. Now, which of you two is Jaspal?
Jaspal	I am Jaspal, Your Highness.

King	I believe some jewels were stolen from your mistress.
Jaspal	Yes, Your Highness.
King	Did you steal them from her?
Jaspal	No, Your Highness.
King	Tell me your story. Where were you when you heard the jewels were missing?
Jaspal	I had just arrived at my mistress' house for work. She was sitting in her bedroom, crying and holding her empty jewel box.

King	When did you last see the jewels?
Jaspal	The night before. It was my turn to help my mistress to get dressed for a party. I did her hair and gave her the jewels she asked for.
King	What jewels did she wear?
Jaspal	A diamond tiara for her hair, a diamond ring and a necklace of gold elephants.
King	And when your mistress was ready for the party, where did she put the jewellery box?

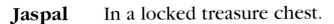

Jaspal	In a locked treasure chest.
King	And where did she put the key?
Jaspal	I don't know, Your Highness. She has never told me where the key is kept.
Sita	Of course not! She wouldn't trust you.
Judge	Silence until the King asks you to speak.
King	Very well, Sita. And when did you last see your mistress' jewels?
Sita	I live at my mistress' house and wouldn't dream of stealing a grain of rice from her. I saw the jewels the day before they were stolen. My mistress asked me to clean some silver bangles for her. I sat in her bedroom and cleaned them all. There were twenty silver bangles.

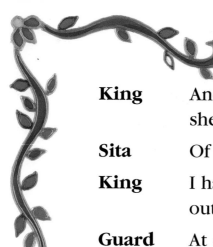

King	And did your mistress count them when she put them back in the box?
Sita	Of course not. She trusts me.
King	I have heard enough. Guard, take them outside.
Guard	At once, Your Highness.
Judge	So who is the thief, Your Highness?
King	I can't tell you now, but I'll be able to tell you in the morning. Guard, bring in Jaspal and Sita again and bring me my box with the magic sticks.
Guard	Very well, Your Highness.
Narrator	As Jaspal and Sita come back into the room the guard hands the box to the King. The King takes out two sticks and holds them up in front of Jaspal and Sita.
King	Jaspal and Sita, I am going to give each of you a magic stick. As you can see, the two sticks look exactly the same but, because they are magic, one of the sticks will grow in the night. Whoever has that stick is the thief. Guard, take them to their rooms, then bring them back here in the morning.
Guard	I will, Your Highness.
Narrator	All night long, the judge wondered who was the thief – Jaspal or Sita.

The next morning, the King went to his throne room. The judge watched as Jaspal and Sita were brought into the throne room to hand their magic sticks to the King.

Guard	Here are Jaspal and Sita, Your Highness.
King	Now. Last night these two magic sticks were the same size. In my right hand I have Jaspal's stick. In my left hand I have Sita's stick. Look at them now.
Judge	Sita's stick is shorter! You said that whoever had the stick that grew would be the thief. Jaspal must be the thief!
King	No. Sita is the thief.
Judge	How can that be?
King	I said that the sticks were magic – but they were not. Sita knew she had stolen the jewels and thought that her stick would grow in the night. So she cut a piece off. Now it is the shorter stick.
Sita	I've been tricked!
King	Jaspal, you may go free. You told the truth. You did not steal the jewels. Guard, take Jaspal back to her mistress' house.
Guard	Yes, Your Highness.
King	You, Sita, will be sent to prison. But first you must tell the judge the whole story.
Judge	Thank you, Your Highness. You are the wisest King in India!

All Aboard the Ark

SHEILA LANE AND MARION KEMP

CAST		
	Noah	Mrs Noah
	Shem	Mrs Shem
	Ham	Mrs Ham
	Japhet	Mrs Japhet
	Hedgehog 1	Hedgehog 2
	Dog 1	Dog 2
	Mouse 1	Mouse 2
	Elephant 1	Elephant 2
	Hamster 1	Hamster 2
	Giraffe 1	Giraffe 2
	Sea-lion 1	Sea-lion 2
	Cat 1	Cat 2

*Noah and his family (Mrs Noah, Ham, Shem, Japhet and their wives) "build" the Ark shape as they sing the first verse of the **All Aboard** song. They put up notices.*

Chorus

    Rock an' roll
    Aboard the floating Zoo,
    Rock an' roll
    Aboard the floating Zoo.

1   The Noahs built a giant Ark,
    Rock an' roll an' rock.
    Gobble, growl, quack and quark,
    Rock an' roll an' roll.

Animals begin to assemble outside the Ark and join in singing

2   The animals came in two by two,
    Rock an' roll an' rock.
    The Noahs cried, "What shall we do?"
    Rock an' roll an' rock.

Chorus

Some animals enter the Ark. The Noah family looks worried. Noah goes out.

    3   The animals came in four by four,
        Rock an' roll an' rock.
        The Noahs cried, "Let's shut the door!"
        Rock an' roll an' rock.

    Chorus

More animals enter the Ark. The Noah family looks very alarmed.

All Noahs   No more! No more! Let's shut the door!

Noah returns carrying three more notices.

Noah   No! No! They must all come in. We must get them properly organised. Now, Ham! Read this.

He holds up a notice.

Ham   "ALL HEAVY ANIMALS THIS WAY." That's a good idea, father. Now then … (*shouting*) All heavy animals this way. Come on, you elephants!

Elephant 1   All right! Elephants can read, you know.

Elephant 2   And elephants never forget!

Ham's Wife   All giraffes! This way!

Giraffe 1   We're not heavy animals.

Giraffe 2   We're just tall.

Ham   Don't start arguing. You'll all be much better off if you do as you're told.

Noah Shem! This one is for you.

He holds up a notice.

Shem "ALL ANIMALS WITH HORNS THIS WAY." Come on you horny beasts. Cows! Reindeer! Rhinos! Over here!

Mrs Shem What about the hedgehogs, Shem?

Shem Ah yes! This notice should say: "ALL ANIMALS WITH HORNS OR PRICKLES WHICH MAKE OTHER PEOPLE UNCOMFORTABLE, THIS WAY!"

Hedgehog 1 We don't make people uncomfortable unless they attack us.

Hedgehog 2   Why is that man saying nasty things about us?

Hedgehog 1   People do!

Noah   Japhet! You must stop the fish from coming aboard.

He hands a notice to Japhet.

Japhet   "ALL FISH MUST MAKE THEIR OWN ARRANGEMENTS!" This notice should say: "ALL CREATURES THAT CAN SWIM MUST MAKE THEIR OWN ARRANGEMENTS."

Mrs Japhet	In that case, we won't have any sea-lions. Go back, sea-lions! You can swim along behind.
Sea-lion 1	But you let the land-lions on board.
Sea-lion 2	So it's not fair to keep us out.
Japhet	You can swim.
Sea-lion 1	But we're mammals. Anyone will tell you that.
Sea-lion 2	Tell him we must have nice rocks to rest on.
Sea-lion 1	Please let her come on board. She won't take up much room.
Sea-lion 2	I can't go without you, dear.
Sea-lion 1	Shh! I'll slip in on the other side. Keep talking.
Sea-lion 2	All right! *(loudly)* What shall I do? I'm not up to long distance swimming these days.
Japhet	Oh, all right then! Come along.
Mrs Noah	Now animals, are you sitting comfortably?
Mouse 1	I'm not!
Mouse 2	I'm sitting very uncomfortably.
Hamster 1	It's this hedgehog!
Hamster 2	We mice and hamsters have such tender skins, Mrs Noah. Please give us a place away from the hedgehogs.
Mrs Noah	Poor little things! Come along over here. This is a nice, quiet corner. Move over, Cat.

Mouse 1	Cat! Cat! Don't say that!
Mouse 2	Oh, Mrs Noah! We can't sit by a cat!
Cat 1	We cats aren't moving.
Cat 2	We like this nice, quiet corner.
Dog 1	Come over here by us … Puss!
Dog 2	We'll lick your fur. We'll make you purr!
Mrs Noah	Yes, that's what I'll do. I'll put you two cats over here by the dogs.
Cat 1	It's not fair! We were here first.
Cat 2	Besides! Dogs chase cats!

Mrs Noah	What nonsense! We're ALL FRIENDS on the Ark. Now! I do believe everyone's sitting comfortably at last.
Noah	At last! Now we can go and get some supper. Come along, family.

All the Noah family, except Mrs Noah, goes out.

Mrs Noah	Now animals! No quarrelling! Particularly you dogs and cats!
Cat 1	Dogs and cats always quarrel.
Cat 2	Well … nearly always … except in stories.
Mrs Noah	Stories! That's a good idea, Puss! Now, you come and tell the animals a story while I go and help with the supper.
Cat 1	What kind of story?
Mrs Noah	A story about … let me see … a story about a cat and a dog … and lots of other animals … with a happy ending.

Mrs Noah goes out.

Cat 2	Let me think … Well … Once upon a time there was a cat, a dog and … a donkey … who all lived together on a farm. Look! Here they come!

Acknowledgements

Stories

The Little Boy's Secret by David L. Harrison, from *The Book of Giant Stories* co-published in 1971 by Jonathan Cape Ltd (England) and American Heritage Press (USA), used by permission of the author; *All the Way from China* by Pat Boran, used by permission of Poolbeg Press Ltd; *Horrid Henry* by Francesca Simon, from *Read Me A Story Please, 50 Readaloud Stories* chosen by Wendy Cooling, used by permission of Orion Children's Books; *Things That Go Bump in the Day* by Tony Ross, used by permission of the author; *Anna's Six Wishes* by Margrit Cruickshank, used by permission of Poolbeg Press Ltd; *Sunkaissa the Golden-haired Princess* retold by Michael Rosen, from *North & South, East & West* edited text © Michael Rosen, used by permission of Walker Books, London; *The Whales' Song* by Dyan Sheldon (Hutchinson), used by permission of Random House, illustrations by Gary Blythe are 'detail' from the originals, used by permission of The Random House; *The Troll's Story* by Vivian French, from *Read Me A Story Please, 50 Readaloud Stories* chosen by Wendy Cooling, used by permission of Orion Children's Books; *The Winter Hedgehog* by Ann and Reg Cartwright (Hutchinson), used by permission of Random House; *The Toad Tunnel* by Anthony Masters, from *Literacy World Fiction Stage 1 Essential Texts Anthology* © Anthony Masters 1998, used by permission of Heinemann Educational Publishers; *The Stranger from Somewhere in Time* from *The Stranger from Somewhere in Time* © Sam McBratney 1994, first published in the UK by Heinemann Young Books, an imprint of Egmont Children's Books :Ltd, used by permission of Egmont Children's Books; *It's Not Fair! ... that I'm little* by Bel Mooney, published by Egmont, used by permission of David Higham Associates on behalf of the author; *The Lion Cub* © 1966 by the Literary Estate of Eilís Dillon, used by permission, detailed information on the author and her works can be found on the WWW at the following address: www.eilisdillon.com; *The Chicken Gave it to Me*, from *The Chicken Gave it to Me*, © 1992 Anne Fine, first published by Methuen Children's Books Ltd and Mammoth imprints of Egmont Children's Books Ltd, London and used by permission of Egmont Children's Books; *The Sea of Tranquility* by Mark Haddon, used by permission of HarperCollins Publishers Ltd; *Bill's New Frock*, from *Bill's New Frock*, © Anne Fine 1989, published by Methuen Children's Books Ltd and Mammoth, imprints of Egmont Children's Books Ltd and used by permission of Egmont Children's Books; *Metalmiss* by Linda Pitt, used by permission of Andersen Press Limited; *Stone Fox* © John Reynolds Gardiner 1980, used by permission of HarperCollins Publishers.

Poetry

The Whale's Hymn from *Gargling With Jelly* by Brian Patten (Viking, 1985), © Brian Patten 1985, used by permission of Penguin Books Ltd; *Breakfast Time*, used by permission of The Society of Authors as the Literary Representative of the Estate of James Stephens; *The Engine Driver* from *Tiny Tim* (Heinemann), used by permission of David Higham Associates on behalf of the author; *A Dog's Life* from *Gargling With Jelly* by Brian Patten (Viking, 1985), © Brian Patten 1985, used by permission of Penguin Books Ltd; *Picking Teams* from *Please Mrs Butler* by Allan Ahlberg (Kestrel, 1983), © Allan Ahlberg 1983, used by permission of Penguin Books Ltd; *The Leader* from *The Kingfisher Book of Comic Verse*, © Roger McGough as printed in the original volume, used by permission of PFD on behalf of the author; *Allosaurus* and *Tyrannosaurus*, text © 1988 Jack Prelutsky, from *Tyrannosaurus was a Beast: Dinosaur Poems* illustrated by Arnold Lobel, used by permission of Walker Books Ltd., London; *Some One*, used by permission of The Literary Trustees of Walter de la Mare, and the Society of Authors as their representative; *Spaghetti* from *Where The Sidewalk Ends* by Shel Silverstein, © 1974 by Evil Eye Music, Inc., used by permission of Edite Kroll Literary Agency Inc.; *Scissors* from *Please Mrs Butler* by Allan Ahlberg (Kestrel, 1983), © Allan Ahlberg 1983, used by permission of Penguin Books Ltd; *Kite* © June Crebbin, from *The Jungle Sale*, used by permission of the author; *Grandad* by Kit Wright, used by permission of the author; *The Sound Collector*, © Roger McGough as printed in the original volume, used by permission of PFD on behalf of the author; *Daddy Fell into the Pond*, used by permission of The Society of Authors as the Literary Representative of the Estate of Alfred Noyes; *Gran, Can You Rap?* © Jack Ousbey, used by permission of the author; *To a Squirrel at Kyle-Na-No*, used by permission of A. P. Watt Ltd on behalf of Michael B. Yeats.

Plays

Real Dragons Roar by Jacquie Buttriss and Ann Callander, from *Literary World Fiction Stage 2 The Alien and Other Plays*, used by permission of Heinemann Educational Publishers; *The Magic Sticks* retold by Robina Beckles Willson from *Literary World Fiction Stage 1 Magic Sticks and Other Plays*, used by permission of Heinemann Educational Publishers; *All Aboard The Ark*, from *Traditional Tales* (part of the *Playmakers* series) published by Cambridge University Press, used by permission of the authors.